LIES YOU LEARNED AT SCHOOL

Michael Powell

FALL
RIVER
PRESS

Written by Michael Powell
Designed by Allen Boe

Fall River Press
122 Fifth Avenue
New York, NY 10011

ISBN: 978-1-4351-1202-5

Printed and bound in Canada

1 3 5 7 9 10 8 6 4 2

Publisher's Note: The views expressed herein are the personal
views of the author and are not intended to reflect the views of the publisher.

Contents

Introduction 6

The Declaration of Independence was
   signed on July 4, 1776 8

There are nine planets in our solar system 10

Water is colorless 12

Ben Franklin's kite was hit by lightning 14

Henry VIII had six wives. 16

Vikings wore horned helmets. 18

An ostrich buries its head in the sand 20

Betsy Ross made the American flag. 22

Goldfish have three-second memories 24

Nero fiddled while Rome burned 26

Rudolph the Red-Nosed Reindeer is male 28

Two plus two equals four 30

The universe began with the Big Bang 32

Chameleons change color to match their backgrounds 34

Albert Einstein discovered relativity. 36

Mount Everest is the tallest mountain in the world. 38

Gravity in space is zero 40

Napoleon was French. 42

The United States is a democracy 44

The Nazis invented the Fascist salute 46

Airplanes fly because of the Bernoulli Principle 48

Roman emperors spared lives with a "thumbs up" 50

Shakespeare wrote, "Shall I compare thee to a rose?" 52

Sir Alexander Fleming discovered penicillin. 54

The Great Wall of China is visible from the
   moon with the naked eye 56

Without a spacesuit you would explode in space 58

Lemmings commit mass suicide 60

Mussolini made the trains run on time 62

The Germans invented the concentration camp 64

The Great Barrier Reef is the largest living organism 66

You use only ten percent of your brain 68

All popes in history have been male 70

America was named for Amerigo Vespucci 72

George Washington chopped down his father's
    cherry tree 74

It is dangerous to swim immediately after eating 76

The guillotine is a French invention 78

The Wright Brothers built and flew the world's
    first airplane 80

The United States is composed of fifty states 82

Christopher Columbus discovered America 84

Electrons travel at the speed of light 86

Marie Antoinette said, "Let them eat cake." 88

The last ice age ended 10,000 years ago 90

Reading in bad light will damage your eyes 92

Gold is the only metal that won't rust 94

Human beings evolved from apes 96

Jesus Christ had long hair and a beard 98

There isn't much space inside an atom 100

A penny dropped from the top of the Sears Tower
    could kill a pedestrian on the ground 102

All deserts are hot 104

Baseball was invented by Americans 106

Bats are blind 108

Charles Darwin coined the phrase "survival of
    the fittest" 110

Diamond is the hardest known material 112

George Washington was the first American President. 114

Hair and fingernails continue to grow after death 116

There are three states of matter 118

The Earth is round 120

A duck's quack doesn't echo, and no one knows why 122

Elephants are afraid of mice 124

Lightning never strikes the same place twice 126

Julius Caesar was born by cesarean section 128

Patrick Henry said, "Give me liberty or give me death!" 130

Paul Revere shouted, "The British are coming!" 132

Camels store water in their humps 134

It takes seven years to digest chewing gum 136

Molly Pitcher took her husband's place in battle
    during the Revolutionary War 138

In the 1960s feminists burned their bras 140

Alexander Graham Bell invented the telephone 142

The first Thanksgiving was celebrated by the
    Pilgrims of the Plymouth Colony 144

Thomas Edison invented the electric lightbulb 146

The Colossus bestrode the harbor at Rhodes 148

Witches were burned at the stake in Salem,
    Massachusetts 150

Isaac Newton developed his theory of gravity
    after being hit on the head by an apple 152

Vincent Van Gogh cut off his ear 154

The Earth's magnetic north pole is in the Arctic 156

There are exactly twenty-four hours in a day 158

The Titanic sank because of a huge hole in its hull 160

Introduction

You know that you shouldn't believe everything you read in newspapers, see on TV, or find on the Internet, but you don't expect to have to take the same precautions with what you learned at school.

Well, guess what? There's tons of stuff you've been taught that just isn't true; or, if it is true, it has been dumbed down so much that it's just plain wrong. And that's before you even begin to consider the political and cultural biases that inevitably creep into a nation's collective knowledge, and then sinuously infiltrate the education of subsequent generations.

This book sets the record straight on a classroom full of inaccuracies—from well-meaning health warnings against swallowing gum, reading in dim light, or swimming immediately after a meal, to classroom carelessness that inculcates inaccurate history, sloppy science, wobbly geography, and bad math. It will shake some of the most solid foundations of your knowledge, from the date of the signing of the Declaration of Independence (it wasn't on July 4) to self-evident "truths" such as "two plus two equals four" (not necessarily!).

Many "facts" about our nation have been wrongly reported (in many cases several decades after the event), and cultural memory has a tendency to become simplified or approximated over time to the point of falsehood, such as Ben Franklin's kite getting struck by lightning (it wasn't), Paul Revere shouting, "The British are coming!" (he didn't), or Betsy Ross making the first American flag (she probably didn't).

In some cases, the world and our knowledge of it have simply moved on. For example, there are now only eight planets in our solar system, since Pluto has been reclassified as a "dwarf planet." In other cases, knowledge has been misrepresented: human beings did not evolve from apes but do share a common ancestor with them, and Charles Darwin did not coin the phrase "survival of the fittest."

Sometimes, no matter how you cut it, the "facts" are just plain wrong: not all deserts are hot, chameleons do not change skin color to match their background, and ostriches do not bury their heads in the sand.

"Next you'll be telling us the Earth isn't round!"

Actually, it isn't. Read on, and remember: Don't always believe everything you learned in school!

The Declaration of Independence was signed on July 4, 1776

THE TRUTH

A widely held misconception about the United States' most cherished symbol of liberty is that the Founding Fathers all lined up and signed it on July 4, 1776. The truth is that the final draft of the Declaration of Independence was adopted by the full Congress on that date, but the order to have it "engrossed on parchment" wasn't given until July 19, which means that the official document that is now so carefully preserved in the National Archive wasn't signed until early August.

The process that culminated in the Declaration's adoption began on June 7, 1776, when Richard Henry Lee of Virginia read his resolution to Congress, which began: "Resolved: That these United Colonies are, and of right ought to be, free and independent States, that they are absolved from all allegiance to the British Crown, and that all political connection between them and the State of Great Britain is, and ought to be, totally dissolved." The Lee Resolution was debated until June 11, when consideration was postponed and a Committee of Five was appointed to draft a declaration, whereupon Congress recessed for three weeks.

Thomas Jefferson completed the first draft in seventeen days; the other four members of the Committee of Five (John Adams, Benjamin Franklin, Robert R. Livingston, and Roger Sherman) made some changes. The document was presented to the Continental Congress on July 2.

The Lee Resolution was adopted by twelve of the thirteen colonies, with New York abstaining. After two days of debate, the Declaration was adopted with amendments on July 4, and church bells rang out over Philadelphia.

On July 9, the action of Congress was officially approved by the New York Convention, so on July 19, Congress ordered that the Declaration be "fairly engrossed on parchment, with the title and stile of 'The unanimous declaration of the thirteen United States of America,' and that the same, when engrossed, be signed by every member of Congress."

Finally, on August 2, the journal of the Continental Congress records that "The declaration of independence being engrossed and compared at the table was signed." But not all of the fifty-six signatures that appear on the document were made on this date. Several members of Congress weren't present that day and signed later. These include Elbridge Gerry, Oliver Wolcott, Lewis Morris, Thomas McKean, and Matthew Thornton.

Also, despite the July 19th order of Congress that the document "be signed by every member of Congress" some delegates never signed it at all. These include John Dickinson, who disagreed with independence from Britain, and even one of the Committee of Five, Robert R. Livingston, who felt that Congress should have given the Declaration longer consideration.

There are nine planets in our solar system

THE TRUTH

As of 2006, there are officially only eight planets in our solar system: Mercury, Venus, Earth, Mars, Jupiter, Saturn, Uranus, and Neptune. Pluto, regarded as the ninth planet since its discovery in 1930, has been reclassified as a "dwarf planet."

Over 2,500 astronomers from 75 countries met in Prague at the International Astronomical Union (IAU) in August 2006 and voted to accept a resolution that laid down new scientific criteria for the definition of a planet. They agreed that, in order to qualify, a celestial body should fulfill three requirements. It must:

1. be in orbit around the Sun
2. have sufficient mass for its self-gravity to overcome rigid body forces so that it assumes a hydrostatic equilibrium (i.e., a nearly round shape)
3. have cleared the neighborhood around its orbit

As a result of this ruling, which had been put together by a specially selected committee deliberating for two years, Pluto was downgraded (it failed to meet requirement 3, since it crosses Neptune's orbit) and our solar system lost one of its planets. However, it gained two other dwarf planets: Ceres (which orbits in the asteroid belt between Mars and Jupiter, and accounts for about a third of the belt's total mass) and

Eris (which orbits about three times further away from the Sun than Pluto, but has a greater diameter and mass, making it the largest dwarf planet in our solar system).

An earlier draft of the IAU resolution was passed without requirement number 3, which would have meant acknowledging the existence of twelve planets (the original nine, plus Eris, Ceres, and Charon, Pluto's largest moon).

Just because Pluto has lost its planetary status doesn't make it any less fascinating. The IAU recently described it as "an important proto-type of a new class of trans-Neptunian objects." Reclassification hasn't dimmed astronomers' desires to unlock the mysteries of this distant frozen world.

The IAU is watching closely about seventy further candidates for dwarf planet status, and this may increase to 200 when the Kuiper Belt has been fully explored. The Kuiper Belt is a region beyond Neptune similar to the asteroid belt between Mars and Jupiter, although it is twenty times wider and up to 200 times more massive.

All other objects orbiting the sun are now referred to collectively as "Small Solar System Bodies."

Water is colorless

THE TRUTH

What do we know about water? It is wet, odorless, tasteless, liquid at room temperature, and covers about seventy percent of the Earth's surface. But one thing it isn't is colorless: it's very slightly blue.

Oh sure, you knew that, because it reflects the blue sky: that's why oceans are blue, right? That's not the whole picture, though. Ocean water can often be blue or green because of the presence of organisms such as algae, or dissolved impurities such as copper. Independent of all these factors, however, pure water—water that is free from impurities—is *still* blue.

If you pour yourself a glass of water, it may look clear but it is ever so slightly blue. You can't tell with a glass, but if you peer at a white background through a thirty-foot-long tube full of water, the slight blue tinge becomes perceptible. It can also be seen as the strong blue color that is scattered back from deep holes in fresh snow. How can this be?

Light is composed of small packets, or quanta, of electromagnetic energy called photons. When these photons encounter an object they bounce back (i.e., reflect, as in a mirror), bounce sideways (scatter), pass through, or are absorbed, in varying degrees. The color of something is dependent upon which part of the visible spectrum the absorbed and scattered photons come from. For instance, things (like water) appear "blue" because they absorb photons in the red part of the visible spectrum more easily than blue light (in the case of water, about a hundred times more).

In layman's terms, then it couldn't be clearer: Water looks blue because it *is* blue.

Ben Franklin's kite was hit by lightning

THE TRUTH

A few books, some encyclopedias, and many people still claim that in June of 1752 Ben Franklin's kite was struck by lightning while he was flying it in a thunderstorm, and that Franklin selflessly endangered his life to prove that lightning was an electrical phenomenon. What a lot of nonsense!

If the kite had been hit, the electrical current would have traveled down the string and fried not only whoever was holding the other end, but also most of the bystanders. Since Franklin lived to tell the tale, it is safe to assume that his kite was not hit by lightning.

While it is true to say that Franklin did indeed risk his life, the point of the kite experiment was not to collect electricity from a single lightning strike, but to demonstrate how the string becomes statically charged by the air within a storm cloud. In his writing he advised flying the kite at the beginning of a storm to reduce the risk of being struck.

Franklin describes what happens when a metal key is tied to the end of the string: "And when the rain has wetted the kite and twine, so that it can conduct the electric fire freely, you will find it stream out plentifully from the key on the approach of your knuckle." In other reported versions of the experiment he used an electricity-collecting device called a Leyden jar.

At the top of the kite he "fixed a very sharp pointed wire, rising a foot or more above the wood." Through experimentation he established that conductors with a sharp point discharge the electricity more effectively and at greater distances from the electrical source, and this knowledge helped him to invent the lightning rod.

Franklin admitted that he killed a few turkeys during his experiments and got a few shocking surprises from his Leyden jars, but if he had been struck by lightning while flying his kite, it would almost certainly have marked the swift end to a promising scientific career.

Henry VIII
had six wives

THE TRUTH

It is commonly thought that Henry VIII had six wives. In fact, depending on whom you choose to believe, he only had two, although to reach that number you have to agree with Henry, the Bible, and the Catholic Church—and they contradict each other!

Henry's first "wife" was Catherine of Aragon and he was "married" to her for twenty-four years. When he wanted a divorce, the Catholic Church wouldn't allow it, so he broke away from the Pope and established the Church of England with himself as head. He then got the Archbishop of Canterbury to grant him a divorce, and claimed that he was never married in the first place because Catherine was his dead brother's wife, and a man could not sleep with his brother's widow (because it says so in the Old Testament).

The Pope declared Henry's subsequent marriage to Anne Boleyn to be invalid, because he was already married to Catherine.

His fourth marriage, to Anne of Cleves, was annulled on the grounds that they never consummated the marriage. Also, Anne was already betrothed to another man (Francis, Duke of Lorraine) when she married Henry, which at the time was a legal impediment to their union.

His fifth wife, Catherine Howard, was unfaithful to Henry before and during their marriage, so Henry passed a special law that made adultery by a queen a treasonable offense. This enabled him to have the marriage annulled (after which he had Catherine beheaded).

So, Henry's only two legitimate marriages were to wives three and six: Jane Seymour (married for seventeen months; she died two weeks after childbirth) and Katherine Parr (married for twenty months, before Henry died from an ulcerated leg wound).

During his entire life of fifty-five years, Henry VIII was married for a total of three years and one month to *two* wives.

Vikings wore horned helmets

THE TRUTH

Ask most people to describe a Viking and they'll likely mention horned helmets (along with long boats, marauding, and party-ing hard). But the horned helmet is a myth (as is much of the marauding). Vikings didn't wear them, and the Viking fighting style actually precluded their use.

So where did this misconception come from? It is probably the fault of a Swedish literary society called the *Götiska Förbundet* (Gothic Society), which was created by a number of Swedish poets and authors in 1811. It aimed at furthering national pride through historical study and pro-moting Norse mythology.

Myths have often been associated with classical antiquity in order to legitimize and perpetuate them, and the Vikings have spawned their share. They have often been portrayed wearing winged helmets, especially during the Romantic period, when everyone harked back to classical forms. Horned helmets have been found dating back much earlier to the Bronze Age, and depicted in rock carvings, and it is these earlier references that appear to have been shoehorned into the Viking mythos.

The image of horned helmet-wearing Vikings was disseminated in twentieth-century popular culture through cartoons like *Hagar the Horrible* and the uniforms of professional sports teams like the Minnesota

Vikings. Of course, some Scandinavian people themselves perpetuate the myth, as does their tourism industry.

Helmets took considerable time and skill to make, and were prestige items. Therefore, they were probably worn only by the leading Viking warriors. A lesser Viking could only afford a single weapon and perhaps a shield.

The only extant Viking helmet, which dates from the tenth century A.D., was excavated in 1943 in Gjermundbu, Norway. It has been restored and is now on display in the Museum of National Antiquities in Oslo. It has an iron dome made of four riveted sections, a vizor with eyeholes, and a small spike on the crown—but no horns.

An ostrich buries its head in the sand

THE TRUTH

The ostrich, which can grow to nine feet tall, is famous for supposedly sticking its head in the sand at the first sign of trouble—but it doesn't. Though its brain is only the size of a walnut, an ostrich isn't so stupid as to believe that its problems will go away if it ignores them.

An ostrich actually has three defensive strategies at its disposal. It can run away and maintain a speed of forty miles per hour for thirty minutes. It also has a very powerful kick, which could handily break the legs of many attackers. What's more, it's very good at hiding: when guarding eggs, an ostrich will sit immobile and lay its head and neck along the ground to keep a lookout for predators. An ostrich in this position camouflages itself passably as a bush.

One other behavior may account for the head-in-the-sand myth: ostriches swallow sand and pebbles to aid digestion, and when they do this they sometime lay their head flat on the ground, which from a distance might make them appear to be burying it.

The ugly rumor was generated by the Roman historian Pliny the Elder (A.D. 23–79), who observed these exotic creatures in his thirty-seven-volume epic *The Natural History*, although he makes no mention of sand: "[Ostriches] have the marvelous property of being able to digest every substance without distinction, but their stupidity is no less remarkable; for although the rest of their body is so large, they imagine, when they have thrust their head and neck into a bush, that the whole of the body is concealed." It seems likely that what Pliny assumed was a bush, was in fact the body of an ostrich.

Betsy Ross made the American flag

THE TRUTH

Betsy Ross is famous for helping to design and then sew the first American flag following a secret visit to her Philadelphia home by George Washington and two other members of the Continental Congress in May 1776. Washington is supposed to have shown the newly widowed seamstress a rough design of the flag that included a six-pointed star, and sewing whiz Betsy impressed them all by cutting out a five-pointed star in a single snip. But there is no historical evidence or documentation to support this story.

Betsy was fond of boasting to her grandchildren about her alleged place in history, and it seems that when one of them grew up he helped to promote a family myth to a national one.

Betsy's story was first published thirty-four years after her death (and nearly a century after the alleged event) by her only surviving grandson, William J. Canby, in a paper for the Historical Society of Pennsylvania. Canby was only eleven when his grandmother died.

After Canby's death, his brother George and nephew Lloyd Balderson published a book entitled *The Evolution of the American Flag* (1909), which included a reproduction of a painting by Charles H. Weisgerber depicting the alleged meeting of the committee of Congress with Betsy Ross. The painting, called *Birth of Our Nation's Flag*, then found its way into school textbooks throughout the United States, giving subsequent generations the impression that the event actually took place, even though it is only an artist's interpretation

There are no records to indicate that the Continental Congress had a committee to design the national flag in the spring of 1776; it's highly unlikely that Washington would have headed up such a committee; and there is no mention of a national flag in 1776 in any government records, letters, or diaries from any member of Congress. The first documented mention was the Flag Resolution of 1777. There were at least sixteen other flag makers and upholsterers working in Philadelphia at the time and any one of them could have sewn the first flag. Since there were already many flags in circulation, it is impossible to pin down which was the first.

Goldfish have three-second memories

THE TRUTH

It's an oft-repeated "fact" that goldfish have three-second memories. There are probably hundreds of negligent fish owners out there who think that it's okay to put a fish in a tiny tank, because in the time it takes them to swim around it, they've forgotten where they came from, and are forever exploring exciting "new" vistas. However, scientists have proved that goldfish have quite sophisticated behavior patterns and can remember for up to 2.5 million times longer than previously believed—instead of three seconds, think three months.

In 2003, scientists at the School of Psychology at the University of Plymouth in the United Kingdom tested goldfish by making them operate levers to feed themselves. Once the fish had learned that pressing the lever resulted in food, the scientists restricted the levers' effectiveness to just one hour each day. The fish quickly adapted.

Another team of scientists in Belfast, Ireland has performed tests on goldfish that demonstrate they can learn to avoid parts of their tanks where they receive electric shocks for at least twenty-four hours; what's more, the stronger the shocks, the greater their avoidance. The scientists believe that their finding has significant implications for the sport of angling (fishing with a hook and line): "Angling is not considered to be a cruel sport as it has been assumed that fish cannot perceive pain. This

paper shows that pain avoidance in fish does not seem to be a reflex response, rather one that is learned, remembered and is changed according to different circumstances. Therefore, if fish can perceive pain, then angling cannot be continued to be considered a non-cruel sport."

Nero fiddled while Rome burned

THE TRUTH

During the night of July 18, A.D. 64, fire broke out in the merchant area of Rome. Most of the city was made of wood, so the fire spread quickly, fanned by summer winds. It raged for six days and seven nights, and then abated, only to reignite and burn for three days more. Popular legend has it that the Emperor Nero played the lyre and sang about the destruction of Troy while watching the spectacle from the summit of the Palatine. But the truth is, Nero wasn't even in Rome when the fire started.

Two thirds of Rome was destroyed by the fire. According to the historian Tacitus, "Of Rome's fourteen districts only four remained intact. Three were leveled to the ground. The other seven were reduced to a few scorched and mangled ruins. After the fire the rumor spread that Nero had ordered the city to be torched so that his personal vision for a grander Rome could rise out of its ashes.

While Nero did harbor great ambitions to remodel the city, he was thirty-five miles away at his seaside home in Antium. He returned to the city only when fire threatened his mansion, which linked the Gardens of Maecenas to the Palatine. It was destroyed, but he opened up his gardens to provide relief for the homeless, had emergency accommodations constructed, and distributed cheap grain. Despite these popular measures, the rumors still wouldn't go away.

Finally, Nero decided to blame the fire on the Christians. He ordered the arrest of a handful of followers of this new and obscure sect. They gave false confessions under torture, and soon all Christians became the target of Roman retribution. Hundreds were rounded up and publicly put to death to entertain and pacify the Roman populace, making them some of the first Christian martyrs.

After the fire, Nero's vision became a reality as Rome was rebuilt on a grand scale, with majestic villas and pavilions of marble and stone, wide streets, pedestrian arcades, and lots of water in case of another fire.

Whether or not Nero was responsible for the destruction of the old city remains a mystery, since he was without doubt a vain, cruel, and murderous ruler. But one thing is certain: he definitely did *not* fiddle while Rome burned.

Rudolph the Red-Nosed Reindeer is male

THE TRUTH

The Christmas story and song about a hapless and unpopular reindeer whose shiny red nose singled him out for a very special yuletide mission has become part of contemporary folklore. The story was published as a booklet in 1939 by an American advertising executive named Robert May to be given away to children by department store Santas. Ten years later, the singer Gene Autry recorded a musical version of "Rudolph the Red-Nosed Reindeer" composed by Johnny Marks, and both story and song continue to enchant children and adults today. However, there is one important issue that has long been overlooked, an issue that affects not only Rudolph but Santa's entire sleigh-pulling team: his reindeer are all female.

The reason behind this gender anomaly is antlers. Both male and female reindeer grow antlers, which they shed and re-grow annually, but while the females shed their antlers in the spring, male reindeer lose theirs at the beginning of winter, after the rutting season has ended.

Antlers of mature male reindeer are much larger than those of females, and they are a vital weapon during the ritual combat that establishes which of the dominant males in the herd get to impregnate the females. After the rutting season, the males are exhausted, and their body weight and fat reserves are depleted. The antlers are now redundant and an unnecessary encumbrance. Triggered by male sex hormones, the bone at the base of the antler gets reabsorbed into the body, and the antlers eventually fall off; they don't start growing back until about four months later. After several weeks of sex and violence, the only reindeer with enough energy to drag a sleigh full of gifts would have to be female.

THE TRUTH

"Two plus two equals four" is one of the most basic sums that we learn even before we reach school. It powerfully epitomizes the unequivocal nature of arithmetic, and even truth itself. The result appears so irrefutable that George Orwell famously expressed the idea of freedom in his novel *Nineteen Eighty-Four* as being "the freedom to say that two plus two make four. If that is granted, all else follows." However, two plus two does not equal four. Well, not all the time, anyway.

First, it depends on which "base" you are using. The metric system uses base ten. This means that the value of each position in a numerical value can be represented by one of ten possible symbols: 0, 1, 2, 3, 4, 5, 6, 7, 8, or 9.

However, other bases use a different number of symbols. For example, in Base 2 (or "binary"), only two symbols are used to represent numerical values: 0 and 1. Two would be written like this: "10" (this is "one-zero" not "ten") which means "one from the 2^1 column and zero from the units column." So two plus two in binary would be represented as "one-zero-zero," which means "one from the 2^2 column and zero from the 2^1 column and units column."

Also, if you are working with what statisticians call "significant digits," then numbers can be rounded up or down and represent a band of possible values, allowing for a margin of error. So, for example, "2" may represent a measurement with a margin of error of 0.5, which means the actual value may lie between 1.5 and 2.5; so two plus two lies somewhere between 3 and 5.

In a sense, as soon as measurement is involved, all numbers are just a poor representation, or a rounding up or down, of reality. As soon as we move numbers from the abstract into the real world, errors and approximations creep in. Dealing with numbers is messier that it seems. How else could something like the birth rate in the U.S. (i.e., the average number of children born to a woman) be expressed by a figure as absurd as 2.06?

The universe began with the Big Bang

THE TRUTH

The event that supposedly created the universe is called the Big Bang, but it wasn't that big, and it wasn't a bang. Some scientists don't even believe that it was a unique event, but one stage in an endlessly repeating cycle of universal expansion and contraction.

The Big Bang Theory goes something like this: About 13.7 billion years ago there was a singularity, a point of infinite density and temperature, from which the universe was "born." It then rapidly expanded and cooled, and it has continued to do so ever since.

The Big Bang didn't make a noise because there was no one around to hear it, but also because in the cosmic soup (quark-gluon plasma) a fraction of a fraction of a second after the singularity, there weren't any atoms or molecules to transmit what we call "sound." The universe at that moment consisted of quarks and gluons and other subatomic particles that are the basic building blocks of matter; a split-second later matter predominated over antimatter, giving our universe its character.

Ironically, the name of the theory was coined by one of its earliest opponents, the astronomer Fred Hoyle, who later came to accept it but disparagingly called it the Big Bang Theory to distinguish it from his own steady-state theory, which he had developed in 1948. The steady-state theory posits the continuous creation of new matter as the universe expands. The Big Bang Theory was the new kid on the block, and Hoyle's model remained popular with many cosmologists until the discovery of cosmic microwave background radiation in the 1960s, which is now widely considered the best evidence for the Big Bang.

Maybe it should be called "A Big Bang" rather than "The Big Bang." Mathematical physicist and string theorist Neil Turok, Chair of Mathematical Physics at Cambridge University, thinks there may be many universes and that every few trillion years they collide, creating a big bang. If he is correct, it means that our universe is much older than we thought (over a trillion years old) and that many big bangs have taken place before our own.

Chameleons change color to match their backgrounds

THE TRUTH

Chameleons change color in response to their emotional state, and to light and temperature—*not* because of the appearance of their surroundings.

The basic color of a chameleon depends on its species and its environment, since natural selection has ensured that chameleons that match their surroundings are more successful reproductively than those that don't. But this is as far as the relationship between color and environment goes.

The chameleon has five layers of skin that help to generate various colors. The outer transparent layer of skin doesn't contain any pigmented cells. The next layer contains cells called xanthophores and erythrophores, which have yellow and red pigments respectively. Beneath that is a layer of cells called iridophores, or guanophores, which contain the colorless crystalline substance guanine that can scatter and reflect light, especially blue light. The innermost layer contains pigment cells with granules of melanin that can be moved around within the cell. Melanin is the chemical that makes skin brown in humans.

Chameleons change color to communicate their mood changes to other chameleons. For example, an angry chameleon turns black, whereas a sick chameleon will stay pale because it lacks the energy to change color.

Males change color to signal their interest in females and aggression to other males. When it is cold, they make themselves flat and dark so that they can absorb more heat.

Even Aristotle recognized the emotional component of these color changes as far back as the fourth century B.C. (he correctly observed that chameleons changed color because of fear), but it is the misconception of another Greek writer that seems to have endured in the public perception. Antigonus Carystius (a century after Aristotle) was the first to claim that the chameleon changed to match the color of whatever it rested on.

Albert Einstein
discovered relativity

THE TRUTH

No, he didn't. The principle of relativity (that all movement is relative) was first proposed by Galileo Galilei in the seventeenth century. Einstein postulated the Special Theory of Relativity in his article "On the Electrodynamics of Moving Bodies" published in 1905, and his General Theory of Relativity eleven years later. Strictly speaking, it was Max Planck, in 1908, who coined the phrase "theory of relativity" to emphasize how special relativity (and later, general relativity) uses the principle of relativity.

Galileo (1564–1642) was an Italian physicist, mathematician, astronomer, and philosopher who has been called the Father of Modern Science. While he was alive the theory of absolute rest was the prevailing belief, and had been dominant since the time of Aristotle. This theory states that everything returns to a natural state of rest.

Galileo's principle of relativity, enunciated in 1639 in his *Dialogue Concerning the Two Chief World Systems*, used an example of a ship traveling at constant speed on a calm sea. He stated that an observer below deck would not be able to tell whether the ship was moving or stationary, and therefore that movement is relative. He also supported the theory, put forward by Copernicus a century earlier, that the Earth is not stationary but revolves around the sun.

After Galileo, Sir Isaac Newton observed, "For it may be that there is no body really at rest, to which the places and motion of others may be referred." He found it necessary to invoke the idea of absolute space and of absolute time to which all motion could be referred.

Einstein's Special Theory of Relativity generalizes Galileo's principle of relativity from mechanics to all the laws of physics, including electrodynamics. It was based on two principles that are contradictory in classical mechanics:

1. The laws of physics are the same for all observers in uniform motion relative to one another (Galileo's principle of relativity)

2. The speed of light in a vacuum is the same for all observers, regardless of their relative motion or of the motion of the source of the light

Special relativity overthrew Newtonian notions of absolute space and time by stating that time and space are perceived differently depending on the motion of the observer. It also expresses the famous mass-energy equivalence formula, $E = mc^2$, where c is the speed of light in a vacuum.

In 1916, Einstein expanded the Special Theory into his General Theory of Relativity, unifying special relativity and Newton's law of universal gravitation.

Mount Everest is the tallest mountain in the world

THE TRUTH

Mount Everest is the highest mountain in the world when measuring from sea level, but it isn't the tallest. That honor goes to Mauna Kea on the island of Hawaii.

When dealing with mountains it is important to make the distinction between height above sea level and tallness. The summit of Mount Everest is 29,029 feet above sea level. However, when measured from tip to base, there are taller mountains.

Mauna Kea is an inactive volcano. Its summit is a mere 13,796 feet above sea level, but its base lies on the sea floor almost 20,000 feet below the surface of the ocean, making its total height a staggering 33,465 feet from base to tip.

There is further confusion about where the base of a mountain actually starts. In the case of Mauna Kea, that's easy, because it is on the sea bed. However, Everest shares its base with lots of other Himalayan mountains, which include some of the world's highest peaks. They sit on top of the shared Himalayan foothills, formed at the convergent boundary of two of the Earth's giant tectonic plates.

If you want to be really pedantic, you could argue that a mountain should be measured from its tip to the center of the Earth, but since the Earth is oblate rather than a perfect sphere (see page 120), even this method is flawed. Mount Everest may be the highest piece of land on Earth when measured from sea level, but if you measure from the center of the Earth, even some of the beaches that lie on the Equator are "higher" than mountains in the Himalayas, since the irregular bulging of the Earth at the Equator puts it about thirteen miles further away from the center of the Earth than the North and South poles.

29,029 FT.

THE TRUTH

Gravity is a very important force and it's everywhere—even in space. It is one of the fundamental forces by which all objects with mass attract each other; in layman's terms, it is generally thought of as the agency that gives things "weight." Gravity is responsible for keeping Earth and the other planets in our solar system in their orbits around the sun, and the moon in orbit around Earth.

On Earth we feel heavy because our feet press into the ground, attracted by Earth's gravity (we also exert a tiny gravitational pull on the Earth). The ground stops us from falling any further. However, if you were in the space shuttle orbiting Earth, you wouldn't be flying or floating, you would actually be in free fall. It just so happens that you stay in orbit because the spaceship is traveling sideways at the same rate it is falling, making you feel weightless. Since the spaceship and you are falling at the same speed, you've got nothing to press against to give your body the feeling of "weight."

Gravity does decrease with distance from an object, so the further you are away from Earth, the less you will feel its gravitational pull, but this isn't the reason you feel weightless. Even in space Earth's gravity pulls you toward it. Imagine if you climbed to the top of a ladder that was 300 miles tall. You'd be in space, but you wouldn't be weightless; you would weigh about fifteen percent less than you do on the ground. Your feet would still press into the rungs of the ladder, which would make you feel heavy. You'd have to jump off the ladder to experience weightlessness—right up until the moment you hit the ground.

THE TRUTH

Napoleon is the most famous leader in France's history, but he wasn't born on the French mainland and there is strong evidence that he wasn't even French.

Napoleon was born Napoleone di Buonaparte in Ajaccio, on the island of Corsica. Corsica is located in the Mediterranean, west of Italy, southeast of France, and north of the island of Sardinia.

Two questions are pertinent to Napoleon's nationality: was he born before or after the island was sold to the French by Genoa; and was the island even Genoa's property to sell in the first place?

Until 1768, Corsica belonged to Genoa, which was an independent republic state in Liguria on the northwestern Italian coast. Genoa came into existence in the early eleventh century as a self-governing commune within the old *Regnum Italicum* (the medieval Kingdom of Italy). Corsica was still an important trading center when Napoleon was born. However, after the decline of the Genoan Republic, Corsica was eventually given to France in the Treaty of Versailles on May 15, 1768. The treaty stated that France would occupy Corsica until Genoa could pay back what it owed to France. In reality this meant that Corsica was sold to France in return for cancellation of Genoa's debts.

Napoleon was born on August 15, 1769, but his detractors believed that he lied about his birth, and that he actually had been born the previous year while Corsica still belonged to Genoa. This would have made him Genoan.

However, there is another complication. Filippo Antonio Pasquale di Paoli drove the Genoese from the island, and Corsica declared its independence in November, 1755. The Corsicans did not recognize Genoese sovereignty over the republic. Genoa ceded Corsica to the French because it knew that it had effectively lost control of the island already, and was therefore giving away something it no longer had. All the Treaty of Versailles did was allow the French to occupy Corsica without military retaliation from Genoa.

Finally, there is the argument that, although Corsica became occupied French territory, it wasn't formally incorporated into France until the Congress of Vienna in 1815. So even if Napoleon was born in 1769, as he claimed, in all likelihood he wasn't really French at all.

The United States is a democracy

THE TRUTH
The United States is most certainly *not* a democracy, nor has it ever been; it is a constitutionally limited federal republic set up under a constitution adopted in 1787 by a Constitutional Convention.

Remember the Pledge of Allegiance: "and to the Republic for which it stands"? The American republic was formed to protect liberty, not democracy. In fact, the word democracy doesn't appear in either the Constitution or the Declaration of Independence.

The Founding Fathers recognized the flaws of democracy, namely that "government by the people" and especially "rule of the majority" would inevitably lead to the kind of tyranny that was suffered by the colonies under King George. They knew that the "majority" could be just as tyrannical and as big a threat to individual liberty as any king or dictator. This is why they divided the government into three power-sharing branches to balance the competing interests of the people, and enshrined certain inalienable individual liberties in the Bill of Rights.

The Constitution is explicit about the kind of government it establishes: "The United States shall guarantee to every state in this Union a Republican Form of Government" (Article IV, Section 4).

There are many examples of distinctly undemocratic processes supported by the Constitution, the Electoral College being the most obvious. Certain states achieve an importance that is disproportionate to their population. Everyone knows that the early primary states are not a representative sample of the country, and yet an early win or defeat in one of them can decide which candidates become the chosen runners in the subsequent Presidential campaign. Politicians may argue that having to impress the people of Iowa is a good test of their ability to "relate to the common people." This may well be true, but it isn't democratic. Neither is giving each state the same number of senators, regardless of its population—though this can be seen as a good thing because it is supposed to protect the interests of the smaller states.

Strictly speaking, even the freedom of speech enshrined in the First Amendment is undemocratic, because it protects the individual against the majority. Pure, unchecked democracy is not all it's cracked up to be and, arguably, is not worth fighting for.

The Nazis invented the Fascist salute

THE TRUTH

The straight-armed salute made infamous by the Nazis and Mussolini's Fascists during World War II has its origins in an ancient Roman oath gesture, but the main impetus for its revival came from post-revolutionary France. Similar gestures were popular in the late-nineteenth century in nationalist and socialist movements, and for several decades it was used by schoolchildren throughout America for the Pledge of Allegiance.

The salute is supposed to have been used in ancient Rome. There isn't a great deal of evidence to support this, although on Trajan's Column in Rome some images can still be seen of soldiers raising their arms toward their leader in approval.

The association between the salute and the ancient Romans was cemented by some of revolutionary France's most influential paintings. In Jacque-Louis David's *The Oath of the Horatii* (1784), a central piece of pre-revolutionary propaganda, Roman heroes take an oath of allegiance to the republic with outstretched arms, raised slightly above shoulder level, and with flat palms. Eight years later David's *Tennis Court Oath* depicts members of the revolutionary assembly using the same gesture. David later painted several images of Napoleon being saluted by his soldiers in a similar style.

By the end of the nineteenth century, the gesture had become popular with several mass movements, including the Olympic Movement. It was later adopted by the Italian Fascist party and the Nazi party in homage to the Roman Republic.

In 1892, American Baptist minister Francis Julius Bellamy wrote the Pledge of Allegiance, which appeared for the first time in the September 8th edition of that year in a nationally circulated religious magazine called *Youth's Companion*. For the last four years the magazine had been selling American flags to public schools to boost subscriptions. The Pledge and "flag salute" (or "Bellamy Salute" as it later became known) were created for the celebration of the 400th anniversary of Christopher Columbus's 1492 voyage.

The Bellamy Salute is clearly described in an 1892 issue of *Youth's Companion*: "At a signal from the Principal the pupils, in ordered ranks, hands to the side, face the Flag. Another signal is given; every pupil gives the flag the military salute—right hand lifted, palm downward, to a line with the forehead and close to it. Standing thus, all repeat together, slowly, 'I pledge allegiance to my Flag and the Republic for which it stands; one Nation indivisible, with Liberty and Justice for all.' At the words, 'to my Flag,' the right hand is extended gracefully, palm upward, toward the Flag, and remains in this gesture till the end of the affirmation; whereupon all hands immediately drop to the side."

The Bellamy salute was used by children throughout the U.S. until as late as June 22, 1942, when President Franklin D. Roosevelt replaced it with the hand-over-the-heart gesture because of its similarity to the Nazi salute. In fact, around the same time interventionist propagandists exploited this similarity by photographing prominent opponents of America's entry into the war, such as Charles Lindbergh, with arm raised in a pledge but with the flag cropped out to give the false impression that they were aligned with the Nazis.

Airplanes fly because of the Bernoulli Principle

THE TRUTH

You probably learned at school that planes fly because of the shape of their wing: the top of the wing is rounded and the bottom of the wing is straighter. This means that air has further to travel over the top of the wing than the bottom, creating more pressure underneath which gives the lift. This is called the Bernoulli Principle, but it is a relatively minor component in airplane flight. The major principle is much simpler: it's called the Coandă effect.

The Coandă effect, also known as "boundary layer attachment," refers to the tendency of a stream of fluid to stay attached to a convex surface, rather than follow a straight line in its original direction. It is named for Romanian aerodynamics pioneer Henri Coandă, who was the first person to recognize the importance of this principle for aircraft development.

Coandă built the first jet-propelled aircraft, the Coandă-1910. He was ground testing it in December, 1910, when he briefly took off and then crashed in flames. However, while airborne he observed that the hot gases from the engine appeared to hug the sides of the aircraft, thus causing the fire. He spent many years researching this effect, which was later named for him.

You can observe the Coandă effect yourself without crashing a plane. Run a faucet so that there is a thin steady trickle, and then slowly bring a horizontal glass tumbler in contact with the water flow. The water will immediately wrap around the bottom of the tumbler and flow around it rather than fall straight down from the sides.

On an airborne plane, the air hugs the top of the wing so tightly that huge amounts of air flowing over it are forced down toward the ground, resulting in lift (in accordance with Newton's third law of motion, which states that for every action there is an equal and opposite reaction). The same principle explains how a racing car is kept pinned to the ground by a negative-lift wing (i.e., an airfoil).

THE TRUTH

The phrase *pollice verso*, which means "with a turned thumb," was used in connection with Roman gladiatorial combat, but it is unclear whether the thumb was turned up, turned down, held horizontal, or hidden inside a clenched fist to indicate positive or negative outcomes. *Pollice infesto*, another expression, means "with hostile thumb," but there is no agreement on the actual gesture.

In his *Satire III*, Juvenal writes that the thumbs down signified that the losing gladiator's life was to be spared, and the thumbs up meant he should be killed. Martial says that mercy was shown by the waving of handkerchiefs, rather than gesturing with the thumb, and that spectators lifted their clenched fists, the fight was to continue. Pliny, in his *Natural History*, makes reference to "a proverb that bids us turn down our thumbs to show approval," while Horace speaks of giving approval in sport "with both thumbs" (*Epistles*, I.18.66).

However, the mistaken notion that thumbs down meant death has been perpetuated by a famous nineteenth-century painting that now hangs in the Phoenix Art Museum in Arizona. In 1872 the French history painter Jean-Léon Gérôme created the work entitled *Pollice Verso*, which depicts the Vestal Virgins indicating death to a fallen gladiator in the arena. They lean forward, with their arms extended, fists clenched, and thumbs sticking downward in a dramatic representation of a stabbing action.

Hollywood producers showed the painting to Ridley Scott when they wanted to persuade him to direct the movie *Gladiator*. While researching the movie Scott undoubtedly became aware of the uncertainty surrounding the thumb gesture, but in the end he chose to have Commodus indicate "thumbs up" in sparing Maximus, reasoning that to do otherwise would have caused confusion with an audience.

And so the misapprehension continues.

Shakespeare wrote "Shall I compare thee to a rose?"

THE TRUTH

Shakespeare's great love poems have been extolled for over 400 years. They've been copied, quoted—and misquoted. "Shall I compare thee to a rose" is arguably the most famous line, but Shakespeare never penned any such thing.

However, in "Sonnet 18" he wrote:

> Shall I compare thee to a summer's day?
> Thou art more lovely and more temperate.
> Rough winds do shake the darling buds of May,
> And summer's lease hath all too short a date.

In _Romeo and Juliet_, Juliet says "What's in a name? That which we call a rose by any other name would smell as sweet; So Romeo would, were he not Romeo call'd . . ."

Then, of course, there is Robert Burns's 1794 song "O, my luve's like a red, red rose, That's newly sprung in June."

It seems the three sources have somehow become muddled together to create what could be called a "viral phrase" that was never written.

Other much misquoted lines from Shakespeare include:

"Alas poor Yorick. I knew him well" from *Hamlet*. The correct line is "Alas poor Yorick. I knew him, Horatio."

The expression "gilding the lily" is a misquote from a speech by Salisbury in *King John*: "To gild refined gold, to paint the lily, To throw a perfume on the violet . . . Is wasteful and ridiculous excess."

From *Macbeth*, "one fowl swoop" is a corruption of Macduff's lament upon hearing that his family and servants have all been killed:

> All my pretty ones?
> Did you say all? O hell-kite! All?
> What, all my pretty chickens and their dam
> At one fell swoop?

(The "swoop" alludes to the rapid descent made by a hunting bird [such as a kite] when capturing prey.)

Hamlet said "to the manner born," not "manor," and Queen Gertrude's "The lady doth protest too much, methinks" often has "Methinks" as the first word.

The opening lines of *Richard III* are often misrepresented by being cut short: "Now is the winter of our discontent" means nothing without the rest of the sentence: ". . . made glorious summer by this son of York."

One of Falstaff's lines from *Henry IV, Part I* often suffers both word order change and abbreviation: "The better part of valor is discretion, in the which better part I have saved my life" is often reduced to "discretion is the better part of valor." Also, he was being ironic, since he had just avoided death on the battlefield by pretending to be dead.

THE TRUTH

The accidental "discovery" of penicillin by Scottish pharma-cologist Alexander Fleming in September 1928 is heralded as the beginning of modern antibiotics. But Fleming wasn't the first person to notice its antibacterial properties. Initially, he predicted that penicillin would not be important in treating infection due to the difficulty of producing it in large quantities, and because he didn't believe it would survive long enough in the human body to fight bacteria. He was wrong on both counts. Besides, penicillin had already been used for centuries to fight infection.

In the late nineteenth century, Ernest Duchesne, a young French doctoral student at the Military Health Service School of Lyon, observed how Arab stable boys at the army hospital actively encouraged the growth of mold on their saddles for the treatment of the horses' saddle sores. He was informed that Bedouin tribesmen in North Africa had been making a restorative tincture from the mold on their donkey harnesses for generations. He prepared a solution of the mold, and injected it into diseased guinea pigs, and they all recovered. Barely out of his teens, Duchesne submitted his findings in his doctoral thesis but the importance of his discovery went unnoticed.

Thirty-one years later (and sixteen years after Duchesne's death from tuberculosis), Fleming made history by accident. In September 1928, he returned to his laboratory at St. Mary's Hospital in London after a long weekend hiking to discover that a batch of petri dishes containing cultures of staphylococci bacteria had become infected with a blue-green mold. He threw them in disinfectant and only later noticed that in one of the dishes the bacteria had been unable to grow around the mold. He managed to isolate an extract and then identified it as a member of the *Penicillium* group (named from the Latin word *penicillius*, which means "brush").

Initially, the scientific community ignored Fleming's discovery, since it seemed fanciful to suggest that mold could treat infection. It wasn't until World War II that a team led by Dr. Howard Florey at Oxford University created penicillin in sufficient quantities to conduct clinical trials. In 1941, the team moved to the United States where pioneering methods of mass-culture were already being developed, and they used a strain of penicillin from a moldy cantaloupe in a Peoria, Illinois market to culture large quantities. In subsequent clinical trials, penicillin was found to be the most effective antibacterial agent to date; it went into mass-production, and was available in sufficient quantity to treat Allied soldiers wounded on D-Day.

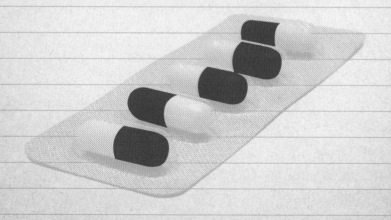

The Great Wall of China is visible from the moon with the naked eye

THE TRUTH

Traveling from Earth to the moon, you lose the ability to distinguish the Great Wall of China with the naked eye long before reaching your destination.

The myth that you can see the Great Wall from the lunar surface was started in 1938 by an American traveler, adventurer, and author named Richard Halliburton, when he published his *Second Book of Marvels*, which states, "Astronomers say that the Great Wall is the only manmade thing on our planet visible to the human eye from the moon." It has persisted ever since as an urban legend, and the mistake was repeated during the 1980s when it appeared as one of the supposed facts in the popular board game Trivial Pursuit.

Space begins about sixty miles from Earth's surface, which is surprisingly close. The British astronomer Fred Hoyle is reported to have remarked, "Space isn't remote at all. It's only an hour's drive away if your car could go straight upwards." From this short distance away, it is possible to pick out many manmade objects such as motorways, railways, cities, fields, and the Great Wall. However, you only have to travel another few thousand miles away before all man-made objects fade from view.

According to NASA, "The Great Wall can barely be seen from the Shuttle, so it would not be possible to see it from the Moon with the naked eye."

A typical Shuttle orbit altitude is about 200 miles. By the time you reach the Moon (which is over a quarter of a million miles away), it is almost impossible even to see the continents.

NASA astronaut Alan Bean has described the view of Earth from the Moon: "The only thing you can see from the moon is a beautiful sphere, mostly white [clouds], some blue [ocean], patches of yellow [deserts], and every once in a while some green vegetation. No manmade object is visible on this scale."

THE TRUTH

You wouldn't survive for very long in space without a spacesuit, but you wouldn't explode, nor would your eyeballs pop out of their sockets, despite what you my have seen in the movies (*Total Recall*, anyone?). In fact, if your helmet came off during a space-walk, you would stand a good chance of surviving if you could get back to the spacecraft quickly (as Dave Bowman did in the movie *2001: A Space Odyssey*).

Death *could* occur, but it wouldn't be instantaneous. You would have about fifteen seconds of useful consciousness and then, with your brain starved of oxygen, you would slip into unconsciousness and die within a few minutes. You would lose body heat, but not instantaneously as this would occur by radiation only (convection and conduction require molecules, which are limited in space). So you would die of oxygen starvation rather than being frozen.

On Earth our bodies are subjected to about fifteen pounds of pressure per square inch. In space pressure per square inch is nearly zero, so the soft tissues in your body would swell, but you wouldn't burst. Your blood and other bodily fluids would boil because of the change of pressure (since under low pressure liquids turn into gases—i.e., boil—without the application of heat), but if you went into recompression they would return to normal. (Chimps and monkeys have been exposed to a virtual vacuum for up to two minutes without suffering permanent damage.)

In training, astronauts have had suit gloves pop off in a vacuum and suffered no permanent damage. During suit testing trials at NASA, an astronaut suffered pressure-suit failure in vacuum conditions and reported feeling saliva boiling off the surface of his tongue, but he didn't explode. Instead, he lost consciousness after fifteen seconds and later made a full recovery.

On August 16, 1960, USAF pilot Joe Kittenger made a high-altitude parachute jump from *Excelsior III*, a helium balloon. He was wearing a pressure suit, and on his ascent to 102,800 feet he lost pressure in one of his gloves. His hand swelled and he lost function, but it did not explode.

If you held your breath it is conceivable that your lungs could rupture as the gas expands, but if you breathed out, the air in your lungs would escape without causing damage. Also your eardrums might rupture and you would suffer severe sunburn owing to exposure to intense ultraviolet radiation.

Lemmings commit mass suicide

THE TRUTH

Lemmings have become symbols for the stupidity of the herd mentality, as they run headlong in large numbers from the top of tall cliffs and hurtle to their self-inflicted deaths or drown in the water below. However, this is an urban legend. Lemmings do occasionally fall off cliffs, but only by accident and when their population density is very high.

In years when breeding conditions encourage a surge in population, lemmings are forced to migrate to areas of lower population density in search of food. When they do they travel in medium-sized groups, not in a teeming mass. Invariably, when they reach a cliff, they cannot proceed any further, so as numbers increase, some unlucky lemmings at the front accidentally fall to their death, pressed forward by the crowd. But it isn't suicide. When food is scarce, lemmings are far more likely to kill each other than themselves.

The mass-suicide myth was reinforced first by a 1954 *National Geographic* article, which showed large numbers of lemmings jumping off Norwegian cliffs. This was followed in 1958 by a Disney documentary involving lemmings called *White Wilderness*. It was filmed in Alberta, Canada, which is not a native habitat for lemmings, so they had to be imported specially (i.e., bought from Inuit children). The movie makers wanted to film a sequence of lemmings migrating in large numbers, so they placed them on a large arctic turntable and filmed them from several angles, to simulate a chaotic mass migration.

The suicide sequence was created by the movie crew herding a group of lemmings over a small cliff into a river because they were unable to get "natural" footage of this phenomenon in the wild (since it doesn't happen). At that time, it was standard practice for nature documentaries to include staged footage if the real footage was too difficult to obtain.

In 1991, *Lemmings* became one of the most popular computer games of its time; the object of the game is to prevent swarms of lemmings from mindlessly moving into danger *en masse*.

Mussolini made the trains run on time

THE TRUTH

The expression "even Mussolini made the trains run on time" is often used as a sardonic criticism of government inefficiency contrasted with the super-efficiency of the worst of all possible regimes. However, Mussolini didn't make the trains run on time; he merely took credit for changes mostly put in place before he came to power, and he concentrated on improving select routes at the expense of the rest of the network.

During World War I, the Italian railway system fell into decline, but after the war it improved considerably. When Mussolini came to power in 1922, the first thing he wanted to do was demonstrate that Fascism was of benefit to the Italian people. So, like many dictators before and since, he created the myth of super-productivity and efficiency, making the Italian rail network one of its cornerstones. He took credit for rail improvements, although most of the work had been done before he took power.

His railway "improvements" were mainly designed for outward show, rather than to demonstrate genuine efficiency. For example, Milan Central station, completed in 1931, is a monumental symbol of resurgent power and Fascist triumphalism, with its 650-foot-wide façade, great steel canopies, 24 platforms, and cathedral-like 235-foot vault.

Posters of the time depict Mussolini as a heroic figure benevolently handing out new trains to the Italian people. He did build some imposing central stations, and upgraded the main lines to impress businessmen, politicians, and foreign tourists, but the rest of the network fell into even greater disrepair, and the working conditions for railway staff deteriorated.

Mussolini dissolved the railroad-workers' union and fired nearly 50,000 employees. The number of casualties and accidents soared as he stepped up his cosmetic building program. While a select group of trains for "important" people ran on time, this was at the expense of schedules for trains for ordinary passengers that were regularly shunted into sidings to clear the track for the elite passengers.

The next time you overhear a disgruntled citizen lamenting with irony about how Mussolini made the trains run on time, set him straight.

The Germans invented the concentration camp

THE TRUTH

The Germans got there third. Concentration camps were invented by the Spanish in Cuba in 1895, and then used by the British during the Second Boer War (1899–1902). The first German concentration camps were in Southwest Africa (not Europe). Since World War II the term "concentration camp" has become synonymous with ethnic extermination, but the original intention of these camps was containment (like internment) rather than deliberate extermination, although they led to the deaths of many thousands of innocent people.

In 1868, Carlos Manuel de Céspedes declared Cuban independence from Spain and the emancipation of the slaves. It is calculated that as many as 200,000 Cubans and Spaniards died during the subsequent Ten Years War. In 1878, peace was restored when the Spanish promised extensive reforms, including the abolition of slavery. However, there was another uprising five years later as Cuban independence fighters destroyed Spanish sugar plantations, which led the Spanish governor, Valeriano Weyler y Nicolau (nicknamed The Butcher), to round up large sections of the Cuban population and intern them in camps called *reconcentrados*. He issued an ultimatum: people had eight days to move into the camps, otherwise they would be considered enemies and be killed. With so many crammed together, conditions inevitably deteriorated and became unsanitary, and thousands of men, women, and children died. The Spanish were soon forced to abandon this policy after an international outcry.

The first British "concentration camps" were set up in South Africa during the Second Boer War, in which the Boers (Dutch South Africans) fought a guerrilla campaign for their independence from the British Empire. The camps were originally intended to act as refugee camps to house families who had been forced to flee their homes because of the conflict. The British created the disastrous refugee situation, and made thousands of families homeless with their scorched-earth policy, burning down crops, homesteads, and farms, and killing livestock, in order to flush out the guerrillas. The British built a total of 109 tented camps (45 for Boer internees and 64 for black Africans) housing over 100,000 people. They were poorly run and overcrowded; food was inadequate, and disease spread quickly. Emily Hobhouse, a delegate of the South African Women and Children's Distress Fund, visited some of the camps and her subsequent report caused a domestic and international uproar. British opposition leader Lloyd George accused the government of "a policy of extermination" against the Boer population. Precise figures are not known, but it is believed that more than 40,000 internees perished.

The Germans set up their first concentration camps in 1904 in what is now Namibia; 100,000 Africans died through violence and starvation there. Dachau was one of the Nazis' first European concentration camps, opened in March 1933, initially to house political opponents. Six extermination camps were constructed in Poland for the express purpose of extermination: Auschwitz-Birkenau, Treblinka, Belzec, Sobibór, Lublin, and Chelmno. More than six million people died in these camps.

By the time the Nazis began building concentration camps there was clearly already a well-established precedent for their use, and a knowledge that they led to high rates of mortality. When the camps were liberated after the War, their atrocities should have come as no surprise to the Allies.

THE TRUTH

The largest organism found on Earth can be measured by a variety of criteria, including volume, area, mass, height, and length. The Great Barrier Reef doesn't qualify because it cannot be classed as one living organism: it is composed of millions of separate sea creatures, which makes it a superorganism.

The largest single organism by volume and mass is an Apsen grove in Utah, a clonal colony of a single male Trembling Aspen (*Populus tremuloides*), nicknamed Pando (Latin for "I spread"). All the trees are genetically identical and share the same massive underground root system. The grove covers 43 hectares and is estimated to weigh 6,615 tons. The root system is thought to have come into existence about 80,000 years ago (around the same time that humans migrated out of Africa), making it also one of the oldest known living organisms.

The current top contender for largest organism by area is a giant fungus of the species *Armillaria ostoyae* in the Malheur National Forest in the Blue Mountains of eastern Oregon, which covers an area of over 2,200 acres (equivalent to about 1,665 football fields). Experts disagree about whether the massive underground vegetative system connects all the fungus, or whether it is a series of separate large clonal colonies. The fungus system has been around since about 200 B.C. (about the time the Great Wall of China was completed). Most of the bulk of this organism lies underground, but occasionally, during the fall season, golden-colored "honey mushrooms" appear on the surface of the soil. The mushrooms are edible, though they are an acquired taste.

Not counting multistem clonal colonies, the biggest individual tree by volume is the General Sherman tree, an individual Giant Sequoia located in the Giant Forest of Sequoia National Park in the United States, east of Visalia, California. The volume of its trunk is about 52,500 cubic feet and it is believed to be approximately 2,200 years old.

The tallest living tree in the world is a Mendocino Tree, a coast redwood (*Sequoia sempervirens*) in Montgomery State Reserve near Ukiah, California. It is over 367 feet tall (five stories higher than the Statue of Liberty) and is estimated to be over 1,000 years old.

By volume and weight, the largest known animal ever to have lived is the blue whale; its tongue, alone, weighs as much as an elephant. The greatest officially recorded length for a blue whale is 110 feet 2 inches, with a weight of 210 tons for a pregnant female. The largest land animals alive today are male savannah elephants, which can weigh as much as 27,000 pounds.

You use only ten percent of your brain

THE TRUTH

Wouldn't it be wonderful if there really was ninety percent of our brain somewhere not being used? It would be like discovering that your house was really a hotel with an extra ninety rooms that you'd never noticed before. It's an entertaining fantasy that is encouraged by advertisers to sell us everything from self-help material to breakfast cereal, but it is not true. You use all of your brain most of the time.

During the early 1800s, scientists became fascinated with understanding how localized parts of the brain deal with specific functions. The science of phrenology—deducing human behavior and personality from examining bumps on the skull—flourished.

As our knowledge of brain topography increased, modern scientists discovered that the frontal lobe is associated with reasoning, planning, parts of speech, movement, emotions, and problem-solving; that the occipital lobe is associated with visual processing; and that the temporal lobe is associated with perception and recognition of auditory stimuli, memory, and speech. However, this simplified picture of the brain is not the whole story. Brain imaging with PET (positron emission tomography) scans has shown that even relatively simple mental tasks or thought processes use many parts of the brain at once. A neurological disorder such as Parkinson's disease affects only specific areas of the brain, but it has devastating global consequences.

We only understand a little of how our brains work, but this does not mean that we only use a fraction of them. While it may be true that we can all develop intuitive powers, or teach ourselves to perform an array of new and exciting tasks, that doesn't mean that we suddenly switch a light on in parts of our brain that have previously languished in darkness.

One of the main reasons why the ten percent myth has proliferated is that the alleged untapped potential in our brains has become increasingly associated with paranormal abilities, which are supposed to lie dormant or to have been forgotten by modern humans. Also, people who make a living out of selling self-help material often suggest that we only use a fraction of our brain, and then claim that their methods can somehow magically retrain us to reclaim the so-called unused portion. It is a powerful metaphor that, taken literally, can be as reductive as the phrenology of old.

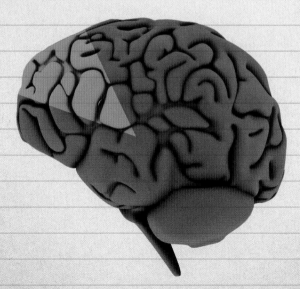

All popes in history have been male

THE TRUTH

There is a persistent and popular belief that a female pope reigned during the ninth century A.D. The story appeared during the Middle Ages, and is supported by several written sources.

The earliest reference to a female pope is in the writing of Martinus Scotus, an eleventh-century monk from the Abbey of St. Martin of Cologne: "In A.D. 854, Lotharii 14, Joanna, a woman, succeeded Leo, and reigned two years, five months, and four days."

In the twelfth century, the scribe Sigebert de Gemlours wrote, "It is reported that this John was a female, and that she conceived a child by one of her servants. The Pope, becoming pregnant, gave birth to a child, whereof some do not number her among the Pontiffs."

The Dominican chronicler Jean de Mailly, writing in the thirteenth century, describes a female pope, but places her reign at the end of the eleventh century.

The most famous account comes from the thirteenth-century Polish chronicler Martin of Opava, who placed a female pope between the reigns of Benedict III and Nicholas I in the 850s. In his *Chronicron pontificum et imperatum* (*The Chronicle of the Popes and Emperors*), he writes: "John Anglicus, born at Mainz, was pope for two years, seven months and four days . . . It is claimed that this John was a woman, who as a girl had been led to Athens dressed in the clothes of a man by a certain lover of hers. There she became proficient in a diversity of branches of knowledge, until she had no equal . . . A high opinion of her life and learning arose in the city, and she was chosen for pope. While pope, however, she became pregnant by her companion. Through ignorance of the exact time when the birth was expected, she was delivered of a child while in procession from St. Peter's to the Lateran, in a narrow lane between the Colisseum and St. Clement's church. After her death, it is said she was buried in that same place."

By the middle of the thirteenth century, the existence of a female pope was widely accepted, and there are many references to a female pope in the later Middle Ages and the Renaissance. During the late fourteenth century, a series of papal busts was commissioned for the Duomo of Siena which included the female pope, named "Johannes VIII, Foemina de Anglia," between those of Leo IV and Benedict III. However, in 1601, Pope Clement VIII had the bust destroyed and replaced by a male figure of Pope Zachary.

Believers in Joan's brief papacy cite an associated custom that allegedly arose of enthroning new popes on an ancient marble throne called the *sedia stercoraria*. It had a hole in the seat so that the cardinals could determine the gender of the pope, before declaring "*Testiculos habet et bene pendentes*" ("He has testicles, and they dangle nicely"). In the 1290s, the Dominican Robert of Usèz had a vision in which he claimed to have seen the seat "where, it is said, the Pope is proved to be a man."

America was named
for Amerigo Vespucci

THE TRUTH

Most people believe America is named for Amerigo Vespucci, the Italian navigator who sailed with Christopher Columbus to the Caribbean and South America in 1499 and 1502. However, new countries or continents were never named for the Christian name of its discoverer; the surname was favored, as in Tasmania (named in 1642 by the Dutch explorer Abel Tasman), or the Cook Islands (named for Captain James Cook, who explored them in 1773). So it would make sense to look for an explorer with a similar surname: that person is Richard Ameryk, a wealthy aristocratic merchant living in Bristol at the end of the fifteenth century, who funded a voyage that reached America two years earlier than Columbus's voyage with Vespucci.

The error originated on a map from 1507, by cartographer Martin Waldseemuller, who made a tentative guess that the word "America" that he inscribed across South America was derived from the Christian name of Amerigo Vespucci. However, in a later edition of his map in 1513, Waldseemuller thought the better of it and reverted to the phrase "*terra incognita*" instead.

Richard Ameryk (c.1445–1503) was the main investor in John Cabot's (Giovanni Caboto) second transatlantic voyage to the North American mainland aboard the *Matthew* in 1497. Cabot landed somewhere on the east coast of Newfoundland on June 24, possibly Labrador, Newfoundland, or Cape Breton Island, and mapped the coastline from Nova Scotia to Newfoundland.

Bristol fishermen had been sailing to Iceland since the 1440s and to the Newfoundland fishing banks since about 1480. Both John Cabot and Christopher Columbus were aware of this, but they believed the Bristol ships had reached Asia.

AMERYK

AMERIGO VESPUCCI

George Washington chopped down his father's cherry tree

THE TRUTH

We all know how the story goes: six-year-old little George chopped down his father prized cherry tree with his new hatchet, and when his father asked him if he knew who was responsible, George replied, "I can't tell a lie, Pa; you know I can't tell a lie. I did cut it with my hatchet." The trouble is that the incident never happened, but the legend has persisted, probably for no other reason than "if the tale isn't true, it should be."

The famous incident was made up by ex-parson turned bookseller, Mason Locke Weems, who first wrote about it in his popular biography of Washington, entitled *A History of the Life and Death, Virtues and Exploits of General George Washington*. It was published in 1800 and became an instant bestseller. One hundred and fifty years after it was first published it had been through eighty-two known editions, including translations into French and German. The last edition appeared in 1927.

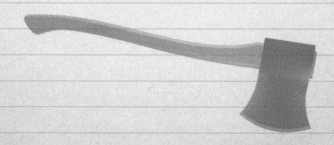

The following passage, which comes a few paragraphs before the cherry tree story, is typical of the florid and hyperbolic writing style that became an immediate hit with his readers:

> Thus, parents that are wise, will listen, well pleased, while
> I relate how moved the steps of the youthful Washington,
> whose single worth far outweighs all the oaks of Bashan
> and the red spicy cedars of Lebanon. Yes, they will listen
> delighted while I tell of their Washington in the days of
> his youth, when his little feet were swift towards the nests
> of birds; or when, wearied in the chase of the butterfly,
> he laid him down on his grassy couch and slept, while
> ministering spirits, with their roseate wings, fanned his
> glowing cheeks, and kissed his lips of innocence with
> that fervent love which makes the Heaven!

Weems's account of Washington humbly praying in the snow at Valley Forge for God's blessing of his troops (made famous by Henry Brueckner's painting in the 1860s) is another piece of pious revisionism, designed to make Washington appear more of a Christian than a deist. Washington regularly attended church, but he didn't take communion, and on his deathbed he didn't ask for prayers or a minister.

With the American population still reeling from the turmoil of the Revolutionary War, people needed a hero and Mason Locke Weems, ever the astute businessman, gave them what they wanted. His book was full of other tales of the selflessness, honesty, and piety of "the greatest man that ever lived."

It is dangerous to swim immediately after eating

THE TRUTH

Generations of well-intentioned teachers and parents have admonished children to wait anywhere between half an hour to an hour after eating before entering the water for a swim. However, there is nothing inherently dangerous about swimming immediately after a meal. This dire warning just doesn't hold any water.

Neither the American Academy of Pediatrics nor the American Red Cross make any specific recommendations to delay swimming after eating. There isn't a single documented case of anyone drowning because they didn't wait long enough after a meal. A study of drownings in the United States found that fewer than one percent occurred immediately after the victim ate a meal, and no causal link was established.

Swimming after a five-course meal wouldn't be very comfortable, but it wouldn't cause you to immediately cramp up and drown. You are more likely to vomit, which *could* lead to problems, but drowning certainly isn't a foregone conclusion. Actually, it is better to swim after eating than on a completely empty stomach, as the low blood sugar level associated with hunger is more likely to cause physical impairment than food.

If you have just consumed a reasonable meal, you will be able to swim recreationally without any discomfort or danger. Your body will divert some of its blood supply to your stomach to aid in digestion, but there

would still be plenty left to provide the rest of your organs with their oxygen requirements.

Drinking alcohol before or during swimming is very dangerous, as it impairs judgment and physical ability. Studies have shown that twenty-five percent of teenage drownings and forty percent of adult drownings are alcohol-related. Nevertheless, you are still more likely to hear dire warnings about eating and swimming.

The guillotine is a French invention

THE TRUTH

The guillotine is a device consisting of a tall vertical frame that houses a heavy diagonal blade. The blade is lifted with a rope and then allowed to fall, severing the head of any victim who lays his or her neck beneath it. It became famous at the time of the French Revolution, and has since become inexorably linked with eighteenth-century France. However, similar devices had already been used in other parts of Europe for centuries. The first documented use of a guillotine-like decapitation machine was reported nearly 500 years earlier in Ireland.

According to Holinshed's *Chronicles,* published in 1577, a guillotine-like machine was used to execute Murcod Ballagh near Merton, Ireland on April 1, 1307. A woodcut in the book clearly shows a contraption consisting of a blade set in a vertical wooden frame.

The Halifax Gibbet in the town of Halifax, West Yorkshire may have been in use as early as 1066, but the first definitive reference to it is found in the sixteenth century. It was a colossal wooden apparatus made out of two fifteen-foot-high uprights sitting on a large four-foot-high platform. An ax head was used as the blade, which slid up and down the uprights. It was used until 1650 when it was removed, some believe, in response to the beheading of British monarch Charles I.

The maiden (also known as the Scottish maiden) was modeled on the Halifax Gibbet. It was introduced to Scotland in the mid-sixteenth century by Regent James Douglas, 4th Earl of Morton. He was later executed by it himself, although he wasn't its first victim, as the legend maintains. It was used to execute over 150 people up through 1708.

A guillotine-like device called the Mannaia was in use in southern France and Italy during the sixteenth century. Its most famous victim was sixteen-year-old Beatrice Cenci, who was executed in Rome on September 12, 1599 for killing her father, the sadistic Count Cenci, who had raped her. She became the subject of many dramas, including Percy Bysshe Shelley's tragedy, *The Cenci*, in 1819.

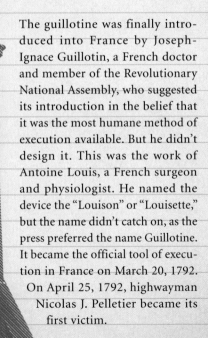

The guillotine was finally introduced into France by Joseph-Ignace Guillotin, a French doctor and member of the Revolutionary National Assembly, who suggested its introduction in the belief that it was the most humane method of execution available. But he didn't design it. This was the work of Antoine Louis, a French surgeon and physiologist. He named the device the "Louison" or "Louisette," but the name didn't catch on, as the press preferred the name Guillotine. It became the official tool of execution in France on March 20, 1792. On April 25, 1792, highwayman Nicolas J. Pelletier became its first victim.

THE TRUTH

The Wright brothers were first to invent aircraft controls that made mechanical fixed-wing flight possible, but they were not the first to build and fly experimental aircraft.

The first records of human flight come from fifth-century China, and there are many reports since of kites, gliders, and several unmanned contraptions. However, there are at least five manned flights that predate the twelve-second flight above the beaches of Kitty Hawk, North Carolina, on December 13, 1903, that assured Wilbur and Orville Wright's fame.

On October 9, 1890, French aviator Clément Ader made the first manned, powered, heavier-than-air flight of a significant distance (165 feet) in a bat-winged monoplane called the *Éole*. It had a wingspan of fourteen yards and a four-blade propeller powered by a four-cylinder lightweight steam engine. The flight wasn't publicized at the time because it was a military secret. According to reports, seven years later Ader flew a different machine for over 650 feet.

In the spring of 1899, Gustave Albin Whitehead and Louis Darvarich made a motorized flight together in a steam-powered monoplane in Pittsburgh. They flew about half a mile, at a height of 25 feet, before crashing into a building. Then, on August 14, 1901, Whitehead flew his

"Number 21" aircraft for a distance of 2,625 feet at a height of 50 feet, and landed safely. It was reported in the *Bridgeport Herald* newspaper but no photographs were taken of the plane airborne.

On September 30, 1899, British aviation pioneer Percy Pilcher intended to give a public demonstration of his newly completed triplane. He had already flown it successfully in private, but on the day of the demonstration a broken crankshaft led him to fly a glider instead, so as not to disappoint the small crowd of potential sponsors. He crashed and died from his injuries two days later, without ever having flown his triplane in public. In 2003, aeronautical engineers at Cranford University built a replica of this plane and flew it for one minute and twenty-six seconds, without the 25-knot wind that assisted the Wright brothers at Kitty Hawk.

In the first years of the twentieth century, Richard Pearse, a reclusive farmer from Waitohi, New Zealand, made several flights in a monoplane with a wingspan of about 250 feet, as well as a sophisticated hinged ailerons that allow him to contro lift. He took no photographs and none of his records remain, but in the 1950s twenty-one men and women who had been children at the time gave corroborated eyewitness accounts that he flew on March 31, 1902 and traveled around 350 yards.

Lyman Gilmore, from Grass Valley, California, claimed to have flown his steam-powered airplane a short distance on May 15, 1902. There were no witnesses. There are photos from 1898 showing his plane, but none show it airborne.

The United States is composed of fifty states

With the admission of Alaska and Hawaii into the Union in 1959, the U.S. grew to fifty states, the number represented by the stars on the current American flag. However, four of these states—Virginia, Kentucky, Pennsylvania, and Massachusetts—use the official title "Commonwealth."

Washington, D.C., also part of the U.S., is a federal district under the authority of Congress. It is governed by a mayor and thirteen-member city council and it is represented in Congress by an elected, nonvoting Delegate to the House of Representatives. Residents have been able to vote in Presidential elections since 1961.

The picture of the United States becomes more complex when one considers its additional commonwealths and dependent areas. Puerto Rico is a commonwealth associated with the U.S. Its indigenous inhabitants are U.S. citizens. Puerto Ricans can't vote in U.S. Presidential elections but they have a nonvoting resident commissioner to the House of Representatives. Dependent areas include American Samoa, Baker Island, Guam, Howland Island, Jarvis Island, Johnston Atoll, Kingman Reef, Midway Islands, Navassa Island, Northern Mariana Islands, Palmyra Atoll, Puerto Rico, Virgin Islands, and Wake Island. Territories that have concluded a Compact of Free Association with the U.S. include Palau (effective October 1, 1994), the Federated States of Micronesia (effective November 3, 1986), and the Republic of the Marshall Islands (effective October 21, 1986).

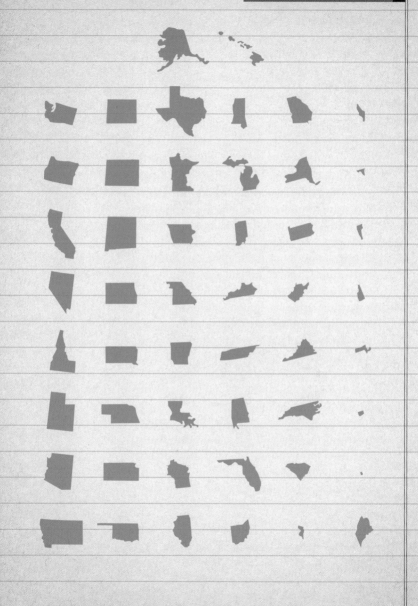

THE TRUTH

Everyone knows the first two lines of the poem: "In fourteen hundred ninety-two, Columbus sailed the ocean blue." He is famous as the first European explorer to land in America. In fact, at least two people may have beaten him to it: their names are Leif Erikson and Zheng He.

Leif Erikson (c.970–c.1020) was a Norse explorer. Norse sagas describe how he established a settlement at Vinland on the east coast of America. Leif, who was born in Iceland, was the son of Erik the Red, who was also an explorer and the son of a Norwegian outlaw who had been exiled to Greenland. Leif spent some time in Norway serving King Olaf I, then he returned to Greenland and set out exploring with thirty-five crew members in A.D. 1003. The first land he reached was covered with flat and shiny rocks, so he named it Helluland (Hell Land, which could be the present day Baffin Island). Next he reached land that was flat and wooded, which he named Markland (which is thought to be Labrador). Finally, they wintered in a place he called Vinland because one of his crew discovered grapes.

During the 1950s and 1960s, explorer Helge Ingstad and his wife, archaeologist Anne Stine, located a Norse settlement at the northern tip of Newfoundland, known as L'Anse aux Meadows, which many believe to be Vinland. In 1964, Congress designated October 9 as "Leif Erikson Day," which is observed in several states.

Between 1405 and 1433, the Chinese explorer Zheng He (1371–1435) made seven epic voyages from China to many places throughout the South Pacific, the Indian Ocean, Taiwan, the Persian Gulf, and Africa using ships and navigational techniques that were years ahead of their time. A small group of scholars led by Gavin Menzies, a former British Navy submarine commander, believe that Zheng He reached America in 1421, seventy-one years before Columbus, and that he also left some settlements in South America. Menzies set out his case in his book, *1421: The Year China Discovered America* (2003). In 2006, a prominent Chinese lawyer and collector named Liu Gang unveiled a map drawn in 1763. The map purports to be a reproduction of a 1418 map made by Zheng He, and it shows the continents with sophisticated detail that the Europeans didn't achieve until a century later.

Electrons travel at the speed of light

THE TRUTH

The electron is a fundamental subatomic particle that carries a negative electrical charge. It has a wide range of speeds, and while it can approach the speed of light (approximately 186,000 miles per second), it can never actually reach it.

The electron derives its name from ἤλεκτρον, the Greek word for amber. Amber has played an important role in the discovery of electrical phenomena. The Greeks observed that rubbing a piece of amber on fur made it produce tiny sparks when it came in contact with a grounded surface (i.e., it became statically charged).

Albert Einstein's Theory of Special Relativity states that the speed of light in a vacuum is constant within all inertial frames and that it is the ultimate speed limit. Electrons move faster as you add energy to them, but the faster they travel, the greater the energy required to make them go faster still. Mass increases with speed, so an infinite amount of energy would be required to make an electron reach the speed of light.

An electron whizzing around a hydrogen atom travels at about a hundredth the speed of light. However, Niels Bohr, who established the Bohr model of the atom, suggested that electrons could only travel at certain quantized speeds and energies, as well as at certain specific distances from the nucleus, otherwise they would spiral inward as they lost energy, implying that all matter is inherently unstable. He proposed that electrons gain and lose speed and energy by making quantum leaps, jumping from one orbit to another.

The innermost electrons of atoms of elements with a large atomic number (such as uranium) travel close to the speed of light, but they never reach it.

When a current flows through a wire, it travels at about 75 percent the speed of light, but the speed at which the electrons travel (the "drift velocity") is relatively very slow. For example, when you pass a steady current of 10 amps through a copper wire with a radius of 1 mm, the drift velocity is only about 0.024 cm per second.

Technically, an electron can attain or exceed the speed of light in a medium other than a vacuum. The speed of light passing through air or water, for example, is slightly slower than the speed of light in a vacuum. In a nuclear reactor, a charged particle such as an electron can pass through an insulator at a speed greater than the speed of light *in that medium*. The electromagnetic radiation this particle emits as a result is known as Čerenkov radiation, which causes the characteristic blue glow of a nuclear reactor.

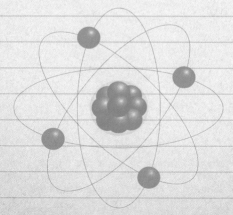

Marie Antoinette said, "Let them eat cake."

THE TRUTH

The supposedly glib remark *"Qu'ils mangent de la brioche,"* which translates as "Let them eat cake," has become synonymous with Marie Antoinette, the wife of eighteenth-century French King Louis XVI, and it epitomizes the contempt with which the French aristocracy held the ordinary people. However, if the phrase isn't apocryphal, it wasn't Marie Antoinette who said it, but a French queen from an earlier time. It had already been in circulation for decades before it is supposed to have been uttered in 1789 in response to hungry peasants begging at the gates of the palace.

Jean-Jacques Rousseau mentions a version of the remark in his twelve-volume autobiographical work *Confessions*. In Book VI, which was written around 1767, he recalls, "At length I recollected the thoughtless saying of a great princess, who, on being informed that the country people had no bread, replied, *'S'il ait aucun pain, donnez-leur la croûte au loin du pâté'*" ("If they don't have bread, give them the crust of the pâté"). Marie Antoinette didn't arrive in France from her native Austria until 1770, so Rousseau couldn't have been referring to her. Lady Antonia Fraser, who has written a biography of Marie Antoinette, believes that Rousseau was referring to Queen Marie Thérèse, the wife of the Sun King, Louis XIV.

Another version in popular circulation is "*Qu'ils mangent de la brioche.*" This is generally translated as "Let them eat cake," even though brioche is a kind of sweet egg bread. In the late 18th century, French law required bakers to sell loaves and fancier products such as brioche at fixed prices, to discourage them from stocking only the more luxurious products in favor of cheaper staples. So the phrase might have meant "Let them buy cake at the same price as bread." Other historians argue that brioche was much closer to white bread than the modern richer version we eat today. So the remark may have been a genuine attempt at kindness, rather than a cynical dismissal.

THE TRUTH

Despite global warming, we are still in the same ice age that began with the formation of the polar ice caps. According to scientists, an ice age is defined as a period in the Earth's climate cycle when there are polar ice caps. We are currently in an interglacial period, which means that within an ice age the continental ice sheets, polar ice sheets, and alpine glaciers retreat as global temperatures rise.

The colder periods during ice ages are called "glacials" and the warmer periods are called "interglacials." Our current interglacial began ten thousand years ago when the ice began to retreat. There were at least four major ice ages in the Earth's past. Outside these periods, the Earth seems to have been ice-free even in high latitudes where temperatures are traditionally cooler.

Scientists believe that the earliest ice age, called the Huronian, occurred between 2.7 to 2.3 billion years ago during the early Proterozoic eon. The next one (and the most severe) occurred from 850 to 630 million years ago (the Cryogenian period), during which the Earth is thought to have been entirely covered with ice (according to the Snowball Earth Theory, which helps to explain the presence of sedimentary deposits of glacial origin at tropical latitudes). This ice age ended rapidly, as water

vapor returned to Earth's atmosphere, and a recent theory suggests that the end of the ice age was responsible for the subsequent Ediacaran and Cambrian explosions (periods of rapid diversification of organisms, as seen in the fossil record).

Earth has experienced a fluctuating series of glacials and interglacials during the last several million years. Our present ice age began 40 million years ago with the formation of an ice sheet in Antarctica. During the late Pliocene, around 3 million years ago, ice sheets spread in the Northern Hemisphere, and this has continued during the Pleistocene. Since then, ice sheets have advanced and retreated in cycles of 100,000 years. The most recent glacial period ended about 10,000 years ago.

Reading in bad light will damage your eyes

THE TRUTH

There are lots of old wives' tales about eyes and what you should and shouldn't do with them. Reading in poor light has been shown to have no long-term adverse effect on eyesight. It does as much harm to your eyes as taking a photo in poor light does to your camera.

Reading in poor light may give you a headache and cause temporary eyestrain, but it won't cause permanent eye damage. It makes it harder for your eye to focus its lens, so the muscles in your eye have to work harder (hence the increased strain). It also decreases the rate of blinking, which can lead to discomfort as the eye dries. If you must read in low light, make sure you blink regularly, rather than stare wide-eyed for extended periods.

Here are some more myths about your eyes:

Sitting too close to the TV is bad for children's eyes: There is no evidence that this is the case. Children's eyes are able to focus without eyestrain at much shorter distances than are adult eyes. If a child sits too close to the TV it may be an indication that he or she is nearsighted and needs glasses, but this is not a direct result of sitting too close to the screen.

If you go cross-eyed and the wind changes, you will stay that way: The only danger associated with going cross-eyed is if a person does it while he or she is performing a task that requires good vision to maintain safety. For example, going cross-eyed while driving would be inadvisable!

If you have poor eyesight, your children will inherit this trait: Poor eyesight does have a hereditary component, but it doesn't follow that all children of parents with poor eyesight will inherit it.

Eating carrots improves vision: Vitamin A is a fat-soluble vitamin required for vision, reproduction, cell growth and differentiation, and a healthy immune system. Carrots are rich in vitamin A, but most people get enough in their daily diet, independent of carrot eating. Too much vitamin A can be toxic and is associated with various health problems, including an increased risk of bone fractures and birth defects.

Gold is the only metal that won't rust

THE TRUTH

The only metallic element that can rust is iron, since rust is a series of iron oxides formed by the reaction of iron with oxygen in the presence of water. Many other metals undergo equivalent oxidation, but the resulting process is called corrosion.

Gold is a metal highly resistant to oxidative *corrosion*, but it is not the only one. Other highly corrosion-resistant metals include platinum, tantalum, rhodium, palladium, and iridium. They are in the group called "noble metals."

Oxidative corrosion results from a metallic element's interaction with oxygen (i.e., oxidation). Gold does not corrode because its atoms do not bond with those of oxygen.

Gold is the most nonreactive of all metals, but it can react to chlorine, fluorine, aqua regia (a mixture of three parts concentrated nitric acid and one part concentrated hydrochloric acid), and cyanide. Gold dissolves in mercury, forming amalgam alloys, but it does not react with it.

Platinum, which is rarer and more expensive than gold, is also more durable and equally resistant to oxidative corrosion.

When two metals are submerged in an electrolyte (any substance containing free ions that behaves as an electrically conductive medium) through which an electric current passes, the less noble will experience *galvanic corrosion*. The rate of corrosion is determined by the electrolyte, and the difference in nobility between the two metals as measured in voltage potential. This is the process by which batteries work. Two noble metals, platinum and palladium, are generally less galvanically corrosive than than gold.

Human beings evolved from apes

THE TRUTH

Humans share a common ancestor with modern African apes, as do gorillas and chimpanzees. But humans did not evolve from apes.

Scientists believe this common ancestor existed 5 to 8 million years ago during the Pliocene era, when the species diverged into two separate branches. One of these branches evolved into gorillas and chimps, and the other evolved into early human ancestors called hominids. Since then there have been at least a dozen different species of these human-like creatures, many of which are our close relatives, but not our direct ancestors, since many went extinct without branching off into other species. Our earliest known human ancestors are commonly called "Australopithecines."

Contrary to popular belief, Neanderthals are not human ancestors, either. The DNA extracted from the ribs of a Neanderthal infant buried in southern Russia 29,000 years ago was found to be too distinct from modern human DNA to be related. William Goodwin, of the University of Glasgow, said of his findings: "There wasn't much, if any, mixture, between Neanderthals and modern humans. Though they coexisted, we can't find any evidence of genetic material being passed from Neanderthals to modern humans."

It is possible that some interbreeding took place between Neanderthals and our human ancestors, but any offspring has since died out. Neanderthals and modern humans coexisted for thousands of years long ago, but only humans survived. The last of the Neanderthals died out about 30,000 years ago.

Jesus Christ had long hair and a beard

THE TRUTH

Actually, he had short hair and a beard. When Judas betrayed Jesus in the Garden of Gethsemane, he kissed Jesus to single him out to the Pharisees. Presumably this was because he looked similar to his disciples. The customary appearance for Jewish men at the time in that region was short hair and a beard, and there is no reason to believe that Jesus or his disciples deliberately changed their appearance to make themselves stand out from the norm.

When Jesus was alive, the Hellenistic Greek culture dominated the Eastern Mediterranean area. A large proportion of the Jewish population spoke Greek and embraced Hellenistic culture. Statues dating to this period always depict men with short hair. Furthermore, the Talmud instructs priests to cut their hair every thirty days. According to *Ezekiel* 44:20 in the Old Testament, "Neither shall they shave their heads, nor suffer their locks to grow long." Writing after the death of Jesus, Paul refers to hair length: "If a man has long hair, it is a disgrace to him." It is unthinkable that he would have written this if Jesus had had long hair.

The only time a male Jew would be required to have long hair is if he had taken a Nazarite vow. Jesus was a Nazarene (he was born in Nazareth) but he never took a Nazarite vow. The vow would have forbidden him from drinking wine or touching a dead body, both of which Jesus did.

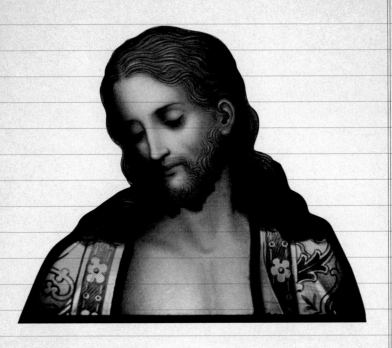

In Eastern lands, a smooth face was associated with effeminacy (and still is), and the beard was cherished as a symbol of virility. To cut off another man's beard was a major humiliation, as described in 2 *Samuel* 10:4–5: "And Hanun took David's servants and shaved off half of their beards, and cut off their long robes in the center, to their buttocks; and he sent them away. And they told David, and he sent to meet them; for the men were greatly ashamed. And the king said, Remain in Jericho until your beard grows; then you shall return." Clearly, it was considered important to wait for the other half of the beard to grow back rather than shave it completely and return immediately.

There isn't much space inside an atom

THE TRUTH

Matter is made up of atoms, but the inside of an atom is mostly empty space, with a few negatively-charged subatomic particles called electrons whizzing around a very small, dense nucleus. If it were possible to remove all the space inside atoms of the Earth so that all the subatomic particles and nuclei were squashed together, the Earth would shrink to the size of a melon.

An atom is about a tenth of a billionth of a yard across, but the subatomic particles are about a million times smaller still. The dense nucleus is made of protons and neutrons and is positively charged, with the exception of the lightest isotope of hydrogen, which has only a single proton.

If an atom were the size of a football stadium, the nucleus would sit at midfield, about the size of a pea, while the electrons would be the size of grains of salt, whizzing in a circular orbit around the nucleus at the back of the stands.

Everything on Earth is made up of these mind-bogglingly tiny particles, separated by vast swathes of space. Superstring theory posits that they aren't particles at all, but tiny loops of string, vibrating in different ways. No one really has a clue about the nature of subatomic particles.

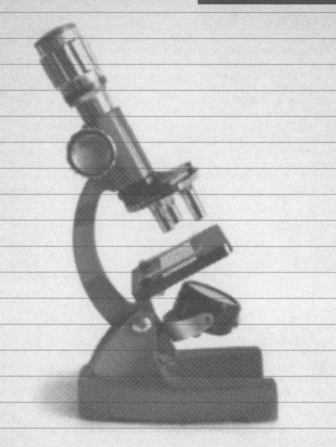

Sometimes they're waves. Sometimes they're particles. Sometimes they're energy. Sometimes they're mass. One physicist called them "the dreams of which stuff is made."

Matter is an illusion of waves and particles. The world we live in isn't as solid and tangible as it might appear.

A penny dropped from the top of the Sears Tower could kill a pedestrian on the ground

THE TRUTH

A penny thrown from the top of the Sears Tower in Chicago wouldn't make a strong enough impact to kill someone on the ground. It wouldn't even break their skin, so it certainly wouldn't break through the sidewalk (as urban legends speculate).

The Sears Tower is 1,353 feet tall. If wind resistance was zero and there was no updraft, the penny would take approximately six seconds to reach the ground, by which time it would be traveling at its terminal velocity of about 280 feet per second. That's not very fast. The muzzle velocity of a .22 caliber handgun is three or four times faster.

However, wind resistance would slow the coin down considerably, since it isn't very aerodynamic.

Louis Bloomfield, a physics professor at the University of Virginia, recently performed an experiment by attaching a coin dispenser to a weather balloon (since he wasn't allowed to drop a coin from a real building). He sent the balloon a couple hundred feet into the air, but he didn't need to send it any higher because the coins reached their terminal velocity within about fifty feet. The coins wouldn't have fallen any faster no matter how much higher they were dropped from.

He was so confident that the coins would be harmless that he attempted to catch them as they fell, and he was struck several times. He reported that "it was like getting hit by a bug . . . it was noticeable, but nothing more. I was just disappointed I hadn't caught the thing. I didn't catch it because I'm a bad catcher and it was a windy day, but basically these things are just fluttering down."

THE TRUTH

The geological definition of a desert is a place that receives less than ten inches of rain each year. Low rainfall isn't dependent on heat, though. The driest place on the planet isn't the sand-swept Sahara, Kalahari, or even the Australian outback: it's Antarctica, Earth's southernmost continent overlying the South Pole. In some parts of this giant frozen desert, it hasn't rained for two million years.

The average yearly total precipitation for Antarctica is about two inches, and the interior of the continent is technically the largest desert in the world. It is sometimes called the White Desert, even though it contains 80 percent of the world's fresh water locked up in its ancient sea ice. Over time, the salt inside the ice leeches out into the surrounding ocean, so old ice can be thawed and drunk. This is how early polar explorers replenished their drinking supplies.

The lowest recorded natural temperature on Earth (-128.6 °F) was in Antarctica in 1983. At 5.4 million square miles, it is the fifth-largest continent in area after Asia, Africa, North America, and South America, but 98 percent is covered by snow or ice, which is 3 miles thick in places, and so heavy that it pushes the land below sea level. If it wasn't for the weight of the ice pressing it down, Antarctica would be 1,500 feet higher above sea level.

Even hot deserts aren't always hot. Nighttime temperatures can fall below freezing because of the low humidity. During the day, the ground absorbs sunlight, heating the air. At night, the reverse happens, and the ground radiates the heat that it has absorbed during the day, causing temperatures to drop quickly. In areas of high humidity, such as the tropics, moisture in the air traps the escaping heat, like a blanket, so there is little temperature difference between day and night. However, in a desert the low humidity allows heat to escape more quickly.

Baseball was invented by Americans

THE TRUTH

The idea that baseball was invented by Abner Doubleday (a Union general in the Civil War) in Elihu Phinney's cow pasture in Cooperstown, New York, in 1839, is a myth deliberately dreamed up in 1907 by U.S. baseball authorities. The modern version of baseball was, indeed, invented in America, but the original version comes from England and was called "base ball."

Records of stick-and-ball games actually date back several thousand years. *The Doomsday Book* of 1085 described the English game of "stool ball" which was also played in America. Governor Bradford at Plymouth Plantation recorded seeing men of the colony "frolicking in ye street, at play openly; some at pitching ye ball, some at stoole ball and such-like sport" on Christmas Day 1621. In 1744, John Newbery of London, England, published *A Little Pretty Pocket Book* of simple rhymes for each of the letters of the alphabet. It includes a woodcut illustration showing a group of boys playing "base ball." The book was reprinted in America in 1762.

In 1905, the Mills Commission, chaired by Abraham G. Mills (the fourth president of the National League), was formed to establish the definitive origin of baseball. On December 30, 1907, the Commission produced a report which confirmed that "the first scheme for playing baseball, according to the best evidence obtainable to date, was devised by Abner

Doubleday at Cooperstown, New York, in 1839." The report concluded, "in the years to come, in the view of the hundreds of thousands of people who are devoted to baseball, and the millions who will be, Abner Doubleday's fame will rest evenly, if not quite as much, upon the fact that he was its inventor . . . as upon his brilliant and distinguished career as an officer in the Federal Army." (Doubleday wasn't a very good general; he earned the nickname "Forty-Eight Hours" for his indecisiveness.)

After Doubleday's death, none of his letters and papers (which include sixty diaries) were found to describe baseball or his part in its invention. The main thrust for choosing Doubleday was the testimony of Abner Graves, a mining engineer from Colorado. Graves was passing through Akron, Ohio, in 1905 when he saw a newspaper advertisement asking for information about the origins of baseball. Graves responded to the advert claiming that he witnessed Doubleday invent the game in 1839 in Cooperstown, New York, and even that he drew a baseball diamond on the ground. Graves, however, suffered from mental illness, which alone calls his account into question.

The real inventor of the *modern U.S. version* of baseball was uncovered in 1947: Alexander Cartwright, a New York librarian. He was a book-seller and volunteer fireman who founded the Knickerbocker Baseball Club (after the Knickerbocker Fire Engine Company) in 1842. In 1845, Cartwright and a committee formally laid down the rules of their stick-and-ball game, which they called the "town game." He was officially credited by the United States Congress on June 3, 1953, with inventing the modern game of baseball.

Bats are blind

THE TRUTH

The expression "blind as a bat" is completely inaccurate because bats aren't blind. They can see reasonably well with their eyes (in laboratory tests they have been shown to distinguish shapes and colors), and when it gets dark they navigate using a sophisticated sonar system called echolocation.

Bats make sounds that measure between 50,000 and 200,000 Hz, which is well beyond the range of hearing in humans (we can perceive sounds between 20 Hz to 20,000 Hz). To echolocate, a bat emits brief pulses of sound—up to 130 each second—and waits for them to bounce back. It can interpret the speed and direction of the returning pulses to understand its surroundings in minute detail. The sonar is so refined that a bat can fly around and catch its prey (insects) in complete darkness.

For centuries, the world's only flying mammal has fascinated and repulsed human beings in equal measure, and several other myths and misconceptions have become associated with it, most notably that bats get tangled in people's hair, drink human blood, are dirty, and spread rabies.

Bats don't get tangled in people's hair; if their echolocation allows them to detect tiny insects, an obstacle as large as a person's head would easily be detected and avoided. Most bats eat insects and fruit. The vampire bat drinks the blood of cattle and other large herbivores as its source of food, but it poses absolutely no risk to humans. Bats are quite fastidious; when they return to their roost, they spend considerable time licking themselves clean. Bats can get rabies, in common with all mammals, but ninety-nine percent of all human fatalities from rabies are from dog bites; furthermore, a rabid bat rarely bites.

Charles Darwin coined the phrase "survival of the fittest"

THE TRUTH

The phrase "survival of the fittest" was not coined by Charles Darwin but by his contemporary, Herbert Spencer. Darwin adopted it in a later edition of *On the Origin of Species* and credited it to Spencer.

In 1859, Darwin published *On the Origin of Species by Means of Natural Selection, or the Preservation of Favoured Races in the Struggle for Life*. His book is the pivotal work in evolutionary biology, and it introduced the theory that populations evolve over the course of generations through a process of natural selection. However, early editions make no mention of the phrase "survival of the fittest."

Herbert Spencer was an admirer of Darwin's work, and first used the phrase "survival of the fittest" in his *Principles of Biology* in 1864, writing: "This survival of the fittest, which I have here sought to express in mechanical terms, is that which Mr. Darwin has called 'natural selection,' or the preservation of favoured races in the struggle for life."

Spencer drew parallels between his economic theories and Darwin's biological ones. Darwin first used the phrase in his fifth edition, published on February 10, 1869: "I have called this principle, by which each slight variation, if useful, is preserved, by the term natural selection, in order to mark its relation to man's powers of selection. But the expression often used by Mr. Herbert Spencer, of the Survival of the Fittest, is more accurate, and is sometimes equally convenient."

Despite this, it must be remembered that the phrase is a metaphor that can be quite misleading as interpreted in popular culture. In Darwin's time "fittest" meant "most suitable" or "most appropriate," while today it tends to be interpreted as "in the best physical shape."

When modern biologists refer to "fitness" they mean reproductive success, which has led to accusations from Darwin's detractors that the expression "survival of the fittest" is ultimately tautological (i.e., it comes to mean "survival of those that are best at survival"). For this reason most biologists favor the term "natural selection" to avoid oversimplification of this complex principle.

Diamond is the hardest known material

THE TRUTH

Until recently diamond was the hardest known material in the world; then, in August 2005, scientists in Germany created a material called ACNR (aggregated carbon nanorods) by heating superstrong carbon atoms at high temperature under immense pressure to mimic the conditions that produce diamonds.

Diamonds are formed deep beneath the Earth's surface under immense pressure and high temperatures. They are brought to the surface by volcanic eruptions, so the only rocks in which diamonds are found are volcanic in origin.

ACNRs were created by simulating this process, using a 5,000-metric-ton multi-anvil press to compress the carbon to 20 (GPa). This is the equivalent of 200,000 times the atmospheric pressure at sea level, or the pressure that occurs over 300 miles below the Earth's surface. At the same time, scientists passed an electric current through a furnace to superheat the material to 3,992 °F.

Carbon can exist in various multiatomic structures with different molecular configurations called allotropes. The three best-known allotropes of carbon are graphite, diamond, and amorphous carbon. Amorphous carbon is carbon that does not have any crystalline struc-

ture. Coal and soot are informally called amorphous carbon but, to be precise, they are a mixture of crystallites of graphite or diamond held together with varying amounts of amorphous carbon. The atomic structure of ACNR consists of sixty atoms arranged in pentagonal or hexagonal shapes.

The measure of resistance to uniform compression of any substance is called its bulk modulus, which is the pressure increase needed to achieve a given decrease in volume. Diamonds have a bulk modulus of 442 GPa, but aggregated diamond nanorods have a bulk modulus of 491 GPa, which is significantly higher. This means that ACNR can scratch diamonds with ease.

THE TRUTH

George Washington was the first President of the United States of America, but he was the sixteenth person to be the American President. The first American President was Peyton Randolph.

Peyton Randolph was the first President of the First Continental Congress, the first de facto national government of America. He presided from September 5 to October 21, 1774, and then again for a few days in 1775 from May 10 to May 23. Another fourteen men succeeded him as presidents of the First Continental Congress, the Second Continental Congress, and the United States in Congress Assembled.

So, when George Washington was sworn in as the first President of the independent United States of America on April 30, 1789, he became the sixteenth American president.

The fifteen men who preceded George Washington are:

First Continental Congress:

Peyton Randolph (September 5, 1774–October 21, 1774)
Henry Middleton (October 22, 1774–October 26, 1774)

Second Continental Congress:

Peyton Randolph (May 10, 1775–May 23, 1775)
John Hancock (May 24, 1775–October 31, 1777)
Henry Laurens (November 1, 1777–December 9, 1778)
John Jay (December 10, 1778–September 27, 1779)
Samuel Huntington (September 28, 1779–March 1, 1781)

United States in Congress Assembled:

Samuel Huntington (March 1, 1781–July 9, 1781)
Thomas McKean (July 10, 1781–November 4, 1781)
John Hanson (November 5, 1781–November 3, 1782)
Elias Boudinot (November 4, 1782–November 2, 1783)
Thomas Mifflin (November 3, 1783–October 31, 1784)
Richard Henry Lee (November 30, 1784–November 6, 1785)
John Hancock (November 23, 1785–June 5, 1786)
David Ramsay (November 23, 1785–May 12, 1786)*
Nathaniel Gorham (May 15, 1786–June 5, 1786)*
Nathaniel Gorham (June 6, 1786–November 5, 1786)
Arthur St. Clair (February 2, 1787–November 4, 1787)
Cyrus Griffin (January 22, 1788–March 4, 1789)

*Due to Hancock's poor health, David Ramsay and Nathaniel Gorham were acting presidents during Hancock's term.

Hair and fingernails continue to grow after death

When you are alive, your fingernails usually grow at a rate of a little more than a thousandth of an inch per day. When you die, your body immediately begins the process of putrefaction and dessication, so the only thing growing in your body is bacteria. As the flesh dries, it pulls in from the extremities. Tissues of the fingers and toes shrink, which makes it appear as though the nails have grown. Likewise with the scalp: as the skin shrinks, it pulls away from the hair, giving the illusion of growth.

Funeral parlors attempt to reduce this skin shrinkage by using moisturizers to provide a barrier and to rehydrate the skin (the top layers of skin are dead, even when we are alive, so it's not as crazy as it sounds).

This myth may have been spawned by Erich Maria Remarque's novel *All Quiet on the Western Front* in which Paul Bäumer, the nineteen-year-old narrator, muses on the death of his friend Kemmerich: "It strikes me that these nails will continue to grow like lean fantastic cellar-plants long after Kemmerich breathes no more. I see the picture before me.

They twist themselves into corkscrews and grow and grow, and with them the hair on the decaying skull, just like grass in a good soil, just like grass . . ."

Johnny Carson also perpetuated the misconception with his famous and oft-quoted quip, "For three days after death hair and fingernails continue to grow but phone calls taper off."

There are three states of matter

THE TRUTH

In the physical sciences, a state of matter is one of the many ways that matter can interact with itself to form a macroscopic, homogenous physical system that has relatively uniform chemical composition and physical properties. At school we are taught that there are three states of matter—solids, liquids, and gases—but this is a gross oversimplification. There are many, many more.

The most common state of matter in the visible universe is not solid, liquid, or gas; it's plasma. Plasma is typically an ionized gas (which has one or more free electrons that are not bound to an atom). All stars are made of plasma. Artificial plasmas are used in plasma televisions and inside fluorescent lamps. We can observe plasma in lightning or St. Elmo's Fire (the bright blue or violet glow that sometimes appears from tall, sharply pointed structures such as lightning rods or a ship's mast, and on aircraft wings).

Other states of matter include: Quantum spin Hall state, superfluid (e.g., fermionic condensate), supersolid, amorphous solid, amorphous glassy solid, amorphous rubbery solid, crystalline solid, plastic crystal, string-net liquid, liquid crystal, supercritical fluid, colloid, degenerate matter, electron-degenerate matter, neutron-degenerate matter, strange matter, Bose-Einstein condensate, quark-gluon plasma, weakly symmetric matter, strongly symmetric matter—and many others.

Recently, superfluids have been used to trap and slow the speed of light. In 1999, Danish physicist Lene Hau led a team which managed to slow a beam of light to about 55 feet per second (compared to its usual speed of 983,571,056 feet per second). Two years later they even managed to stop a beam of light for a fraction of a second.

An amorphous solid has no long-range order of the positions of its atoms. Common examples of amorphous solids are window glass (which flows very slowly; this explains why very old windows are thinner at the top than the bottom) and cotton candy.

A Bose-Einstein condensate is created when a fluid is supercooled to a fraction above absolute zero (-459 °F). Because a fluid at this temperature cannot lose any more of its energy, even through friction, when placed in a container it will overcome gravity and flow out of the container to find its own level.

The Earth is round

THE TRUTH
The Earth isn't a perfect sphere; it is more like a basketball that someone has sat on: squashed at its poles and swollen at the equator. The scientific name for this is an "oblate spheroid."

Isaac Newton was the first person to propose that the Earth is this shape. Geologist Vic Baker at the University of Arizona in Tucson explains why this occurs: "Instead of Earth being like a spinning top made of steel, it has a bit of plasticity that allows the shape to deform very slightly. The effect would be similar to spinning a bit of Silly Putty, though Earth's plasticity is much, much less than that of the silicone plastic clay so familiar to children."

The shape can be proved by observing the position of the stars at different points on the Earth's surface and with precise gravity measurements (objects weigh a fraction less at the equator than at the poles). There is a bulge around the Earth just below the equator, which means that anyone who lives in this part of the world is about thirteen miles higher above the Earth's quasi-spherical surface than are people standing at one of the poles. This also means that some equatorial mountains are actually higher than Mount Everest (see page 38).

Engineer and surveyor Joseph Senne has worked out that the place on Earth closest to the moon and outer space is Mount Chimborazo in

Ecuador, which is 1.5 miles "higher" than Everest (although Everest is still the highest above sea level). Alternatively, if you stood at the Dead Sea, which is the lowest point in the entire world, you would still be three miles further from the center of the Earth than if you were on the summit of Mount McKinley in Alaska.

A duck's quack doesn't echo, and no one knows why

THE TRUTH

The reason no one knows why is because it isn't true. A duck's quack doesn't possess a special acoustic property that cancels out reverberations. This is a much-quoted scientific myth that has been categorically disproved by acoustical engineers at the University of Salford in the United Kingdom.

When a sound is made, it travels away from its source as a sound wave—a series of vibrations or ripples in the air. When sound waves hit obstacles, such as walls, they can be reflected or absorbed, depending on the acoustical properties of their surface. When a loud sound is reflected from a surface that is some distance away from its source, the echo is heard as a separate sound source because it arrives back later.

The Salford scientists placed a duck named Daisy in an anechoic chamber to record what would happen in a room with no reflectors. The walls of the chamber were covered with fiberglass wedges to absorb all the sound. Next, they recorded the duck quacking inside a reverberation chamber where any sound echoes around the space. The quack reverberated as expected. They concluded: "A duck's quack does echo, but in many circumstances will be hard to hear."

THE TRUTH

The sight of a mighty elephant rearing up in distress at a tiny mouse is incongruous and appears in various jokes and metaphors. However, elephantine murophobia has little basis in truth, and probably persists because of its value as a comic morality tale, a warning against hubris, and a reminder that even the mightiest and strongest of beasts has its weaknesses.

One of the earliest references to this myth is in Pliny the Elder's *Natural History*: "They have the greatest aversion to the mouse of all animals, and quite loathe their food, as it lies in the manger, if they perceive that it has been touched by one of those animals" (VIII, Chapter 10).

Pliny also claimed that elephants do not like pigs' squeals, and that pigs were used to deter the animals in battle. "The very least sound, however, of the grunting of the hog terrifies them, where he writes of elephants: when wounded and panic-stricken, they invariably fall back, and become no less formidable for the destruction which they deal to their own side, than to their opponents" (VIII, Chapter 9).

In fact an elephant is afraid of very little, because it is at the top of the food chain. Even big cats pose little threat and would rarely attack an adult elephant. The mouse myth may have arisen from the notion that an elephant is terrified of a mouse running up its trunk. In the unlikely event that this happened, the elephant would simply blow a blast of air

and the mouse would be instantly dislodged. (Besides, it seems unlikely that a mouse would endanger itself in this way.)

Elephants are frightened by sudden, unexpected movements, but their eyesight is poor, and a mouse is so small as to be insignificant. It is conceivable that the sound of unidentifiable scurrying might cause anxiety, in which case it would be frightened by all sorts of small animals, not just mice. However, in most cases an elephant wouldn't even be aware of the presence of a mouse.

Lightning never strikes the same place twice

THE TRUTH

This has to be one of the most popular myths in science. The opposite is true: lightning favors certain places. The Empire State Building gets hit about twenty-five times each year, and several people have been struck more than once.

There are, on average, about 1,800 thunderstorms in progress at any one time around the world with one hundred lightning strikes every second. Objects are more likely to be struck if they are situated in an otherwise featureless landscape or have irregular features. Hence, if you are caught on a golf course during a storm you are at great risk, especially if you are holding a club.

Lightning conductors work on the principle that the metal spike attracts lightning, sparing the building or other object to which the conductor is attached. Because the rod is grounded, the lightning follows the quickest route to the ground, through the wire that runs down the side of the building, protecting those inside and the structure of the building.

The odds of a person getting hit once are 1 in 3 million; twice are 1 in 9 million; three times are 1 in 27 million; four times are 1 in 81 million. Nevertheless, some people have sustained multiple lightning strikes.

The *Guinness Book of World Records* gives the record for being struck by lightning to park ranger Roy Sullivan, who survived seven strikes between 1942 and 1977. He has had his hair set alight, lost his big toenail and eyebrows, and suffered burns. His odds of being struck repeatedly were greatly reduced from the expected 1 in 2.187 billion because of the nature of his job, which exposed him to more storms than most other people.

Julius Caesar was born by cesarean section

THE TRUTH

Cesarean section has been part of human culture since ancient times and its name is often attributed to Julius Caesar, who it is claimed was delivered by C-section. However, while it is possible that Caesar was born in this way, it is unlikely for several reasons.

Cesarean section used to be an exceptional way to come into the world, and so it has been attributed to several outstanding individuals such as gods or heroes. According to mythology, the first C-section was performed by Apollo on his lover Coronis when he delivered Asklepios. Also, Dionysus was taken from the womb of a dead mother.

The procedure's origin was first attributed to Caesar in the first century A.D. by Pliny the Elder, more than one hundred years after Caesar's death. Scholars disagree over the translation of Pliny's claim, with some arguing that Pliny said Scipio was "the first of the Caesars"—the first of Julius Caesar's ancestors to bear the name Caesar, because he was cut from his mother's womb. Others interpret Pliny as meaning that both his ancestor and Julius Caesar were delivered by cesarean.

The first printed illustration of a C-section appears in *The Twelve Caesars* by Suetonius in the second century A.D., which further reinforced the myth.

Ultimately, we can't be certain from what the term "cesarean section" is derived. The true Latin origin could be the root of the verb "*cae-dare*," meaning "to cut," and a Roman legal code called "*Lex Caesarea*," which allegedly made it law that a baby should be cut from the womb if the mother died before giving birth. In this case, the phrase could be interpreted as "imperial law" rather than indicating that Caesar was born this way.

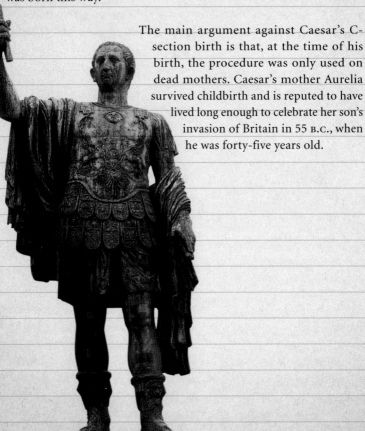

The main argument against Caesar's C-section birth is that, at the time of his birth, the procedure was only used on dead mothers. Caesar's mother Aurelia survived childbirth and is reputed to have lived long enough to celebrate her son's invasion of Britain in 55 B.C., when he was forty-five years old.

Patrick Henry said, "Give me liberty or give me death!"

THE TRUTH

The most famous call to arms uttered by an American revolutionary and Founding Father is credited with convincing Virginia to enter the Revolutionary War, and it has appeared in school history books ever since. However, great orator though Patrick Henry undoubtedly was, these famous words which he supposedly uttered of March 23, 1775, were likely put in his mouth by a biographer four decades later.

Patrick Henry's speeches weren't written down at the time that he made them. They first appeared in print in William Wirt's *Life and Character of Patrick Henry* published in 1817. What Parson Weems did for George Washington's reputation for posterity (see page 74), Wirt did for Henry. Wirt was a gifted lawyer: President Thomas Jefferson asked him to be the prosecutor in Aaron Burr's treason trial, and for twelve years he held the post of Attorney General of the United States. He was very articulate and literate, and many in the South considered him to be one of the chief men of letters of his time. He was ideally suited to recreate—from the recollections of those who were close to events forty years earlier—the impassioned oratory of Patrick Henry.

According to Wirt, Henry's March 23rd speech ended with the rallying cry, "Is life so dear, or peace so sweet, as to be purchased at the price of chains and slavery? Forbid it, Almighty God! I know not what course others may take; but as for me, give me liberty or give me death!" upon which the crowd jumped up and shouted, "To arms! To arms!"

A witness recounting this speech forty years after the event might be forgiven for remembering only a few key ideas or phrases, and a case could be made that the last sentence would have been the most memorable. However, the biggest clue that Wirt chose to end the speech this way is that earlier he compares Henry to the Roman statesman Cato, another famous orator and a firm champion of the Stoic belief that freedom and honor can be achieved through death. In fact, a similar phrase appears in the play *Cato, a Tragedy*, written by English essayist Joseph Addison in 1713, twenty-three years before Patrick Henry was born: "It is not now time to talk of aught/But chains or conquest, liberty or death" (Act II, scene 4). This play was very popular in the colonies, and George Washington had it performed at Valley Forge.

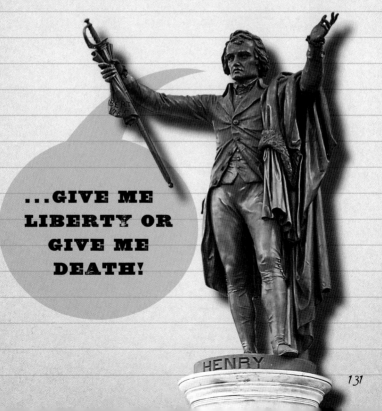

...GIVE ME LIBERTY OR GIVE ME DEATH!

HENRY

THE TRUTH

There is no doubt that Paul Revere was an outstanding organizer and a brave patriot, but many myths surround his "midnight ride" from Boston to Lexington, Massachusetts on the evening and morning of April 18–19, 1775. In fact, he didn't shout "The British are coming!" Neither did he ride from house to house, and he certainly did not reach Concord.

The name of Paul Revere was made famous in 1861 when he became the subject for Henry Wadsworth Longfellow's famous poem "Paul Revere's Ride," which begins:

> Listen, my children, and you shall hear
> Of the midnight ride of Paul Revere,
> On the eighteenth of April, in Seventy-Five;
> Hardly a man is now alive
> Who remembers that famous day and year

Longfellow wrote the poem deliberately to create a stirring patriotic myth to rally Northerners during the Civil War, but for anyone who cares to read the many contemporary diaries and memoirs that record the events of that fateful evening, a different picture emerges of a collective effort rather than the heroic actions of one man.

Scores of riders were involved that night in spreading word that the British were planning a move. Revere was just one of a network of alarm riders who fanned out across the countryside. Even before he had escaped from the city by rowboat, the alarm had been raised by two lanterns being displayed prominently from the steeple of Boston's North Church. Longfellow's poem says that Revere rode to Concord; in fact, he rode to Lexington and then on toward Concord, but he was arrested before he arrived and was led back to Lexington. One of two other riders, Samuel Prescott or William Dawes, raised the alarm in Concord.

Revere didn't go knocking door to door yelling, "The British are coming," because the whole operation was secret, and the area was crawling with British militia. He carried his secret message to special contacts who in turn passed the message further. Also, the colonists still considered themselves British, so he would have referred to the British troops as "regulars." A more likely story is that he was stopped by a guard at Lexington who told him to stop making so much noise with his galloping. Revere replied, "Noise? You'll have noise enough before long. The regulars are out."

Camels store water in their humps

THE TRUTH

Depending on how long ago you went to school, or the quality of your schooling, you may still subscribe to the misconception that camels store water in their humps. They don't; their humps are actually reservoirs of fatty tissue.

The fat in a camel's hump, or humps, can be metabolized and used as a source of energy, but this process actually causes a slight net loss of water. Therefore, a camel has to rely on a host of other adaptations to reduce its body temperature, and to conserve and use water to maximum efficiency:

1. The camel's red blood cells are oval, rather than round as in other mammals. This shape makes them function better in states of dehydration, but they are also able to absorb high levels of water through the cell walls without the cells bursting.

2. The camel can tolerate a much higher variation in body temperature than other mammals. In humans, a body temperature rise or fall of a few degrees can be fatal; a camel's body temperature can comfortably accommodate temperature ranges from 93°F at night up to 106°F during the day, and it will only start to sweat when its body temperature reaches this upper limit, further conserving water.

3. A camel's thick coat reflects sunlight to keep it cool. When sweating does take place it occurs at skin level rather than on its coat, which reduces water loss.

4. A camel's nostrils are adapted so that when it breathes out, a large proportion of the water vapor in the breath is recycled into the body.

5. A camel's kidneys and intestines retain water very efficiently. Urine comes out as a thick syrup, and the feces are very dry.

6. A camel's long legs keep its body away from the hot ground.

So long as they eat sufficient green herbage to give them moisture, in milder conditions camels can survive for ten months without taking a sip of water. They are also able to withstand losing up to forty percent of their body weight without any ill effects. When a camel does get the chance to drink, it takes full advantage of the oppor- tunity, consuming large quantities very quickly. It can drink thirty gallons in ten minutes, and up to fifty gallons over several hours.

It takes seven years to digest chewing gum

THE TRUTH

There are lots of scare stories, urban legends, and well-meaning misinformation centered on swallowing gum, the most pervasive of which is that it sits around in your gut for a long time and is bad for your health. In fact, according to officials at Wrigley, makers of Big Red and Juicy Fruit, it only takes a few days for a piece of gum to pass through your body.

Another popular urban horror story about gum is that dead people have been autopsied and found to have giant sticky balls of the stuff wound around their intestines. This isn't true. There are a handful of rare cases in which very young children (aged between eighteen months to four years old) developed obstruction of the gut after swallowing large amounts of gum, often combined with other objects, but these are exceptional. Gum isn't very sticky when it's inside the stomach and digestive tract, and it doesn't hang around long enough to cause any health problems.

Chewing gum is made up of five basic ingredients, four of which dissolve in your mouth: flavor, corn syrup, sweeteners, and softeners (such as glycerine). The fifth ingredient is gum base, a combination of natural and synthetic gums. This doesn't dissolve in the stomach, but that doesn't mean it stays in your gut for seven years.

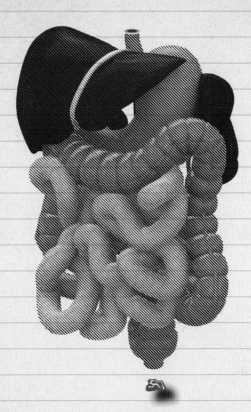

We are told to eat more fiber to improve our digestive system precisely because it is indigestible, so as it travels it scrapes away deposits from the walls of the intestines. Therefore, indigestibility isn't in itself a problem with items of small size. Like fiber, gum simply passes through your digestive tract and comes out the other end looking much the same as when it went in.

THE TRUTH

Molly Pitcher is one of the Revolutionary War's most famous heroines. On June 28, 1778, when her husband died at the Battle of Monmouth, she supposedly dropped the pitcher of water with which she had been quenching the thirst of the troops, and took his place at the cannon. Hundreds of brave forgotten women supplied and supported their men during battle, and Molly Pitcher is a powerful symbol of them all, but she isn't a single person; she's probably an amalgam of at least two brave women, and possibly more.

There is only one eyewitness account of a woman operating a cannon during the Battle of Monmouth (published over half a century after the fact), and it doesn't name her. Joseph Plumb Martin, in his autobiography *Private Yankee Doodle* (1830), writes:

> A woman whose husband belonged to the Artillery, and who was then attached to a piece in the engagement, attended with her husband at the piece the whole time; while in the act of reaching a cartridge and having one of her feet as far before the other as she could step, a cannon shot from the enemy passed directly between her legs without doing any other damage than carrying away all the lower part of her petticoat—looking at it

with apparent unconcern, she observed, that it was lucky
it did not pass a little higher, for in that case it might
have carried away something else, and ended her and
her occupation.

There is little evidence of any Molly Pitcher until the mid-nineteenth century when Nathaniel Currier painted his famous study *Molly Pitcher, the Heroine of Monmouth.*

At least two women may have provided some of the basis for the legend. The first candidate is Mary Ludwig Hays McCauley, a resident of Pennsylvania who was awarded an annuity in 1822 by the Pennsylvania Assembly for her service during the fight for independence. At that time, she was married to William Hays, and after the war, they settled in Carlisle, Pennsylvania (he wasn't killed in battle). When he later died, she married a man named George McCauley, so the annuity is in the name of Mary McCauley, and it was above the normal amount, which may indicate that she was rewarded for special services.

The second candidate is Margaret Corbin. She was born on November 12, 1751, in Franklin County, Pennsylvania. Her husband was John Corbin, and she died in 1789 in Westchester County, New York. Her husband joined the army in 1776 and was a matross—he sponged and loaded the cannons. She was known as a half-soldier and also helped load the cannons.

On November 16, 1776, they were defending Fort Washington, New York, and the gunner was killed, so John took his place and Mary took over her husband's job and was injured, permanently losing the use of her left arm. She was nicknamed "Captain Molly" by the soldiers, and in 1779 the Supreme Court of Pennsylvania awarded her $30 for being a hero. Later, she became the first woman to receive a half-soldier's pension.

In the 1960s feminists burned their bras

THE TRUTH

No serious scholar has been able to prove that feminists publicly burned their bras in the 1960s. The idea of "bra burning" was spread by male headline writers and journalists of the time as a pejorative term, and it has continued to trivialize the aims of the feminist movement ever since.

In the 1960s, radical feminists used protest tactics to highlight gender inequality, and organized a series of provocative and high-profile demonstrations called "zap actions." The first of these to bring national attention to the emerging Women's Liberation Movement was the now famous picket at the 1968 Miss America contest at the Atlantic City Convention Hall. It was organized by New York Radical Women, one of the earliest female liberation groups.

About 400 women gathered in protest on the vast wooden boardwalk outside the venue. They crowned a live sheep Miss America. Women sang songs that parodied the contest and the idea of selling women's bodies: "Ain't she sweet; making profits off her meat." They carried placards with slogans such as "No More Beauty Standards" and "Welcome to the Cattle Auction." Bras, girdles, cosmetics, high-heeled shoes, dish detergent, beauty, housekeeping and erotic magazines, and other objects of female "oppression" were publicly thrown into a "Freedom Trash Can." The organizers intended to set light to its contents, but the

police wouldn't allow this without a permit. The law-abiding protestors obeyed.

New York Post journalist Lindy Van Gelder was sent to cover the demonstration with instructions to write a humorous piece. She made a comparison between women burning their bras and men burning Vietnam draft cards to highlight the need for women's issues to be taken seriously, but this backfired when her headline writer titled her piece "Bra Burners and Miss America."

The 1968 protest was a big success because it attracted attention from every major newspaper in the country, but it also established the myth of bra burning in popular culture.

Alexander Graham Bell
invented the telephone

THE TRUTH

Alexander Graham Bell patented the electromagnetic transmission of vocal sound by undulatory electric current in 1876, but the process was invented and patented five years earlier by an Italian-born inventor named Antonio Meucci. The only reason Bell is remembered today as the inventor of the telephone is because Meucci was too poor to renew his temporary patent when it expired in 1874.

Antonio Meucci was born in Florence, Italy, on April 13, 1808. He studied chemical and mechanical engineering at the Florence Academy of Fine Arts and then spent several years working as a stage technician. In 1834, he constructed an acoustic device similar to the naval pipe-telephone to assist with backstage communication; he was imprisoned in the same year for alleged involvement in the Italian unification movement.

In 1835, Meucci and his wife moved to Cuba, where he constructed a water purification system, experimented with treating patients with electric shocks, and invented the "*telegrafo parlante*" ("talking telegraph") which recorded the human voice. In 1850, he moved to Staten Island, New York and tried to support himself as an inventor.

He constructed his first electromagnetic telephone in 1856 so that he could communicate from his basement laboratory with his wife in her second-floor bedroom where she was bedridden with rheumatoid arthritis. In 1860, he published details of his invention in a local Italian-language newspaper, *L'Eco d'Italia*. During the next fourteen years, he developed more than thirty different telephones, refining his earlier prototype, but he became so poor that he had to rely on handouts from friends.

In August 1870, Meucci successfully reproduced an articulate human voice after transmitting it a mile using a copper conductor. He named his device "*telettrofono*." Just as his fortunes appeared to be improving, he was badly injured in a boiler explosion aboard the Staten Island Ferry, and he was forced to sell some of his inventions to raise money.

On December 28, 1871, Meucci paid $20 to file a caveat for his invention at the U.S. Patent Office, but he couldn't afford the $250 needed for a full patent. The caveat is number 3335, titled "Sound Telegraph." When the caveat expired three years later, he was unable to afford the $10 renewal fee, and when Bell took out his own patent in 1876, Meucci took him to court. But Meucci's lawyer was no match for Bell's expensive legal team, and the judge ruled against him, in what some consider one of the greatest miscarriages of justice in U.S. history. Meucci died penniless in 1889.

Meucci was recognized as the first inventor of the telephone by the United States House of Representatives in House Resolution 269, dated June 11, 2002.

The first Thanksgiving was celebrated by the Pilgrims of the Plymouth Colony

THE TRUTH

Every schoolchild in the U.S. has been taught to associate the first Thanksgiving with the Pilgrims of the Plymouth Colony, Squanto, and the neighboring Wampanoag tribe in the fall of 1621. In fact, that event is more likely to have been at least the sixth Thanksgiving held on American soil.

The first Thanksgiving feast in North America was celebrated by the Spanish conquistador Francisco Vásquez de Coronado and 1,500 men on May 23, 1541, at Palo Duro Canyon, southeast of present-day Amarillo, Texas. The expedition had traveled from Mexico City in search of gold, and the celebration marked the securing of food supplies. In 1959, a patriotic, historical, and educational society called the Texas Society Daughters of the American Colonists commemorated the event as the first Thanksgiving. Also, the Ford County Historical Society has erected a permanent cross outside Fort Dodge, Kansas, 200 miles northeast of Palo Duro Canyon, to commemorate a Thanksgiving service that they believe Coronado held there on June 29, 1541.

If we count Coronado's thanksgivings as a single event, then the second Thanksgiving took place in Florida on June 30, 1564, after French Huguenot Rene Laudonniere and 300 colonists established Fort Caroline six miles up the St. Johns River and were welcomed by Timucuan Indians.

Laudonniere wrote of the feast: "We sang a psalm of Thanksgiving unto God, beseeching Him that it would please His Grace to continue His accustomed goodness toward us."

The third Thanksgiving was held on September 8, 1565, when Pedro Menéndez de Avilés and his 2,000 men are believed to have shared a feast with local tribes at the settlement of St. Augustine in Florida. This event was just prior to Avilés's troops' attack on the nearby French colony of Fort Caroline, and the subsequent bloody massacre of its inhabitants.

A fourth Thanksgiving was celebrated on April 30, 1598, near the site of San Elizario, Texas, by Don Juan de Oñate and some Manso Indians from present-day El Paso. Oñate even had a large church specially erected for the event.

The fifth Thanksgiving took place at Jamestown, Virginia, in the spring of 1610 after English ships arrived with fresh supplies following a famine and a bitter winter that killed most of the settlers.

Even after the 1621 Thanksgiving, the event didn't become a yearly celebration until the nineteenth century. It wasn't recognized as an official national holiday until November 26, 1941, when President Franklin D. Roosevelt signed a bill to establish the fourth Thursday in November as the national Thanksgiving public holiday.

THE TRUTH

Historians Robert Friedel and Paul Israel list twenty-two inventors of incandescent lamps prior to Thomas Edison. Edison's achievement was to produce a long-lasting carbon filament, a better vacuum inside the bulb, and an economically viable power distribution from a centralized source, but he did not "invent" the lightbulb. He simply made and marketed one of the earliest practical examples.

In 1802, the first incandescent light was demonstrated by Humphry Davy, who used a 2,000-cell battery to pass a current through a thin strip of platinum. This discovery led to the revolutionary Davy Lamp in 1816, and laid the foundation for many other inventions during the nineteenth century.

In 1835, James Lindsay publicly demonstrated his constant electric light in Dundee, Scotland, and he claimed the light made it possible to "read a book at a distance of one and a half feet." He didn't take his invention any further, however, and concentrated all his efforts on wireless telegraphy instead.

In 1840, British scientist Warren de la Rue passed an electric current through a platinum coil enclosed in a glass vacuum tube, but the process proved too expensive for commercial use. The following year the first patent for an incandescent lamp was taken out by Frederick de Moleyns.

His device used powdered charcoal heated between two platinum wires contained within a vacuum bulb. This was followed in 1845 by American John W. Starr's patent for an incandescent lightbulb using carbon filaments. In the 1850s, Frenchman Jean Eugène Robert-Houdin publicly demonstrated his incandescent lightbulbs, and Joseph Wilson Swan began working with carbonized paper filaments in an evacuated glass bulb. In 1874, Russian engineer Alexander Lodygin submitted a patent for his filament lamp which used a very thin carbon rod placed under a bell-glass, and a Canadian patent was filed for by a Toronto medical electrician named Henry Woodward and his colleague Mathew Evans, which they later sold to Thomas Edison.

Thomas Edison didn't even start serious research in this field until 1878. Standing on the shoulders of those who had preceded him, Edison filed his first patent application for "Improvement In Electric Lights" on October 14, 1878 (U.S. Patent 0,214,636). He then developed a carbonized bamboo filament that could last over 1,200 hours.

In the same year, Hiram S. Maxim founded the United States Electric Lighting Company, using his patents and those of William Sawyer in direct competition with Edison. There was so much overlapping of technology in this highly competitive area that lawsuits were inevitable. On October 8, 1883, the United States Patent Office ruled that Edison's patents were based on the work of William Sawyer and were invalid, but Edison had this judgment overturned after six years of legal wrangling. Then he teamed up with Joseph Wilson Swan (who had been one of the invention's pioneers) to avoid a patent court battle with him.

Finally, having effectively neutralized rival patent claims, in 1880 Edison patented an electric distribution system and founded the Edison Electric Illuminating Company which allowed him to capitalize on the electric light to such an extent that now many people mistakenly believe him to be the "inventor" of the electric lightbulb.

The Colossus bestrode the harbor at Rhodes

THE TRUTH

One of the Seven Wonders of the Ancient World, the Colossus of Rhodes was a giant statue of the Greek god Helios, which was erected on the Greek island of Rhodes between 292 and 280 B.C. Before it was destroyed by an Earthquake, the statue stood a hundred feet high, making it the tallest statue in the world at the time (and only twenty feet shorter than the Statue of Liberty). However, contrary to its subsequent depiction in literature and art, the Colossus did not stand with one leg on either side of the harbor entrance.

The Colossus was built to celebrate the victory of the islanders against Macedonian King Demetrius I, who besieged Rhodes with his army of 40,000 men (more than the entire population of Rhodes). The city was protected by a strong wall, so Demetrius used a huge wooden siege tower, mounted on top of six ships lashed together, to scale the wall. It was destroyed by a sudden storm. He built a second land-based siege tower called Helepolis ("Taker of Cities"), but the Rhodians stopped it in its tracks by flooding the land outside the walls, turning the earth to mud. After Demetrius abandoned the siege and sailed home, the Rhodians sold his discarded equipment for 300 talents (about $150 million in today's money) to pay for construction of the bronze statue. Helepolis was used for scaffolding, and many discarded weapons were melted down.

There are no ancient accounts of the statue bestriding the harbor entrance gates; this would have meant shutting down the harbor for several years during construction. Instead, it probably stood near the Palace of the Grand Masters, the site of an ancient sanctuary.

The completed statue only stood for fifty-four years. An Earthquake in 226 B.C. caused it to snap at the knees and fall to land. It lay there for over 800 years, where many tourists traveled to marvel at it. This is further evidence that the statue did not straddle the harbor entrance; otherwise it would have fallen into the sea.

Pliny the Elder reported that the fallen statue was so big that most people were unable to wrap their arms around its giant thumb. The Colossus was finally broken up for scrap metal in the seventh century A.D., when the Arabs conquered Rhodes and carted the pieces away on the backs of 900 camels.

Witches were burned at the stake in Salem, Massachusetts

THE TRUTH

A notorious myth of early America is that all those convicted of witchcraft in Salem, Massachusetts in the spring of 1692 were burned at the stake. In fact, not a single one of the fourteen women and five men were burned, since this punishment was not the favored method in the American colonies and English law did not permit it. Most of the condemned were taken to Gallows Hill, a barren slope near Salem Village, and hanged.

The blanket term "burning times" has come to describe the period between the mid-fifteenth century and early eighteenth century when vindictive witch-hunts culminated in the burning alive of thousands of "witches." While it is true that many "witches" were burned alive, it was not the only method. In England and the American colonies, witches were usually hanged; and in France, Scotland, and Germany, they were often strangled to death before being hung and then cremated.

Another common neo-pagan and occultist myth is that nine million people perished during the burning times. This figure is grossly exaggerated, and seems to have been spread after World War II, perhaps in a misguided attempt to put the persecution of paganism on a par with the Holocaust. Reliable scholars estimate that the true figure is closer to 150,000 trials across the whole of Europe, resulting in approximately 75,000 executions.

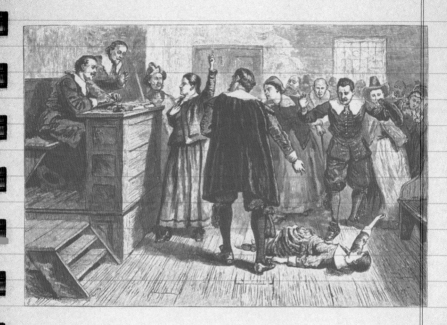

In Salem, Bridget Bishop was the first to be tried. She was found guilty and hanged on June 10, 1692. The others were later led to the gallows on three successive hanging days before the court was dissolved by Governor William Phipps in October. Giles Corey, a man in his eighties, was pressed to death with stones for refusing to cooperate with the court. Today the location of their graves is a mystery, since their relatives were forbidden to bury them in consecrated ground.

Isaac Newton developed his theory of gravity after being hit on the head by an apple

THE TRUTH

We all grew up hearing the popular story that Isaac Newton was struck on the head by an apple as he sat in quiet contemplation beneath a tree, and that in a flash of inspiration he developed his theory of gravity. In fact, the earliest written account of this incident makes no mention of Newton being struck by an apple, and his theory of gravity was more than twenty years in the making.

The apple story first appears in William Stukeley's *Memoirs of Sir Isaac Newton's Life*, published in 1752. Stukeley recounts a conversation he had with his friend Newton on April 15, 1726 (when Newton was in his eighties):

> The weather being warm, we went into the garden and drank tea, under shade of some apple-trees, only he and myself. Amidst other discourses, he told me, he was just in the same situation, as when formerly, the notion of gravitation came into his mind. It was occasioned by the fall of an apple, as he sat in contemplative mood. Why should that apple always descend perpendicularly to the ground, thought he to himself. Why should it not go sideways or upwards, but constantly to the Earth's centre.

The incident is alleged to have occurred in 1666. Newton, then aged twenty-three, was spending eighteen months back at his family home, Woolsthorpe Manor, in Lincolnshire while his alma mater, Cambridge University, was closed because of the plague. However, the theory of universal gravitation didn't spring into his mind at that moment. According to Newton, 1666 was "the same year I began to think of gravity extending to the orb of the Moon," but it took him twenty more years to fully develop his theory of universal gravitation, which states that any two objects in the Universe exert gravitational attraction on each other, with the force having a universal form. Newton left no written record of the apple incident, and he certainly never claimed to have been hit on the head.

153

Vincent Van Gogh cut off his ear

THE TRUTH

One of the "facts" that everyone thinks they know about Dutch artist Vincent Van Gogh is that he cut off his ear. Some people even go as far as to recall that he then mailed the ear to his mistress as a love token. There are two inaccuracies in the previous sentence: he only sliced off the bottom part of his left earlobe, and he gave it to a prostitute for safekeeping.

The infamous ear-cutting incident occurred in the city of Arles in the south of France, on December 23, 1888. Van Gogh had arrived in the city in February of that year and in May he leased four rooms at No. 2 Place Lamartine and demanded that they be painted yellow. In August, he painted *Sunflowers*; he moved into the "Yellow House" in September, and he hung the painting as a welcoming decoration in a bedroom prepared for Paul Gauguin, who joined him in October.

The two men shared quarters and painted side by side for nine weeks. However, by December their relationship had deteriorated badly. Van Gogh, who likely suffered clinical depression, was driven to self-mutilation and sliced off the bottom of his left earlobe after becoming increasingly agitated that Gaugin was going to leave, destroying his dream of founding a Utopian art colony before it had even begun.

Van Gogh wrapped the removed flesh in some newspaper and gave it to a prostitute named Rachel in the local brothel with the instruction to "keep this object carefully." Gaugin left Arles and the two men never saw each other again. Though hospitalized, van Gogh was physically well enough to return to the Yellow House after Christmas, where his mental health continued to deteriorate until he was evicted in March after locals signed a petition to rid themselves of *le fou roux* ("the red-headed madman").

His depression deepened until, on July 27, 1889, he walked into a field and shot himself in the chest with a revolver. He died from his injuries two days later, aged thirty-seven. His beloved brother Theo reported his last words as "*La tristesse durèra toujours*" ("the sadness will last forever").

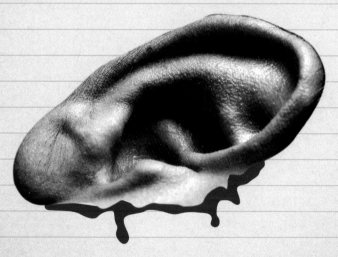

The Earth's magnetic north pole is in the Arctic

THE TRUTH

The Earth's magnetic field makes an area in space around our planet called the magnetosphere. Many school textbooks erroneously represent the Earth's magnetism by a bar magnet running in cross-section through the Earth from north to south, with its ends just below the Earth's crust; however, this image is very misleading. First, the Earth's north and south magnetic poles lie hundreds of miles beneath the Earth's crust. Second, the Earth's northern magnetic pole is actually the south pole of the magnetosphere.

The Earth's molten core is not itself magnetic; it is too hot for that, since all magnetic minerals lose their magnetism at high temperature. The point at which this happens is known as the Curie point. The Curie point of iron, which makes up most of the core, is 1,418 °F, so the Earth's magnetism must be generated by something else.

The Earth can be divided into three large sections: the mantle, outer core, and inner core. The inner core is at the center of the Earth, and although it is its hottest part (12,600 °F—about as hot as the surface of the sun) it is solid, because it is under immense pressure. The outer core of molten iron, at temperatures of between 8,000 °F to 11,000° F, swirls around the solid inner core, and whirlpools are also created

within it by the Earth's rotation. All this swirling creates electric currents which in turn generates the Earth's magnetic field. Geologists call this process the dynamo effect.

However, this magnetic field is not constant in direction. Sometimes the field completely flips and the north and the south poles swap places. This occurs on average every 300,000 years; the last instance was about 780,000 years ago, so we may be due for a reversal soon.

There are exactly twenty-four hours in a day

THE TRUTH

A day is the period of time it takes the Earth to make one complete rotation on its axis. Measured over an entire year, each day is on average twenty-four hours long, give or take a fraction of a second. However, individual days may be as much as fifty seconds longer or shorter than this.

The speed at which the Earth rotates is affected by friction caused by tides, weather patterns, and other geological factors. When scientists discovered this variation, they decided to redefine a second as "the duration of 9,192,631,770 periods of the radiation corresponding to the transition between the two hyperfine levels of the ground state of the caesium-133 atom," rather than as being a fraction of a solar day. The problem with this is that, since the second has now been redefined independently of the solar day, the day that we measure using atomic clocks is drifting apart from it, so scientists have had to add a "leap second" every few years to compensate. There are proposals to change this to a less-frequent "leap hour."

All this is not related to the reason why we have leap years. Every four years (except for some years ending in 00) we add an extra day, February 29, because it takes the Earth 365¼ days to revolve once around the sun.

An average day on Earth hasn't always been twenty-four hours long. A million years ago the Earth rotated faster than it does now, and the day was only eighteen hours long. Also at this time the moon was closer to the Earth (the moon is drifting away from Earth at a speed of about 1.6 inches per year), so its orbit was tighter. Therefore, a lunar month (the time it takes the moon to rotate around the Earth) was only twenty days.

The Titanic sank because of a huge hole in its hull

THE TRUTH

The story of the *Titanic* has fascinated people ever since the ship hit an iceberg off the coast of Newfoundland on April 14, 1912, and sank, killing 1,523 people. Until recently, it was thought that an iceberg ripped a 300-foot hole, in the ship's hull. How else, people reasoned, could the so-called "indestructible" ship have sunk on its maiden voyage?

In 1996, scientists coordinated by the American Discovery Channel finally put this myth to rest. They made several dives and used sonar scanning to map the hull. They discovered that the damage to the vessel was relatively small—they located six narrow gashes in the side of the ship, totaling only about twelve square feet. However, the location of the damage was critical, because the gashes lay directly over six of the ship's sixteen watertight holds.

The scientists also analyzed samples of steel taken from the ship and discovered that, although the steel was the highest quality available at the time, by today's standards it would be considered a hazard, since the high levels of sulfur and oxygen in the metal would have made it brittle and liable to fragment. Also, several of the ship's iron rivets have been examined and found to be substandard.

It seems the *Titanic* simply wasn't anywhere near as strong or well-built as people thought. Within four hours of striking the iceberg, the enormous ship lay on the ocean floor, nearly two and a half miles below the surface of the Atlantic Ocean.